2 - OO

A Source Book of
Canals, Locks and Canal Boats

The waterways network of England and Wales in about 1850, before closures and disuse brought about a contraction. There were few areas of the country not within easy carting distance of navigable water. Compare this with the modern map (p. 19).

A Source Book of

Canals, Locks and Canal Boats

written and compiled by Hugh McKnight

Cruising through the tree-tops in a hired
narrow-boat conversion: the Chirk
Aqueduct which carries the beautiful
Llangollen Canal over the River Ceiriog
near the border between England and
Wales.

WARD LOCK LIMITED · LONDON

Acknowledgements

The author gratefully acknowledges the following
for supplying illustrations: 10, 125, John Humphries; 26, 39, British Waterways Board, *Waterways News*/Hugh McKnight; 30, *Radio Times/
Hulton*; 51, Liverpool City Museum; 53, E. W.
Paget-Tomlinson; 56, Runcorn Public Library; 67,
British Waterways Board; 68, *Express and Star*,
Wolverhampton; 92, *The Times*; 105, Julian Plow-
right; 124, Canadian Government Travel Bureau;
128, Robert Shopland.

All other photographs and the line diagrams are
from the Collection of Hugh McKnight Photography.

The jacket shows a diesel-powered short boat
carrying coal along the Bridgewater Canal at
Worsley.

Introduction

In spite of its title, this book is about rivers as well as canals, for a river system is the basis of Britain's canal network. Yet, but for their lowest tidal reaches, few rivers would be navigable for large craft with any real degree of reliability: thus most of them with which we are concerned here have been considerably canalized by introducing locks, weirs and sections of artificial channel. The most accurate name covering both types of navigation is inland waterway.

Some of our rivers were used for elementary transport purposes long before the start of recorded history. In their natural state they were extremely prone to flooding in winter and could be reduced to a trickle during a dry summer. Nevertheless, they offered local movement facilities for people and goods and supported the establishment of towns and villages along their banks.

The first serious use of inland navigation came during the Roman occupation. There are surviving accounts of the invaders penetrating England's interior up the Thames, while garrison towns like York and Chester were chosen specifically for their situation alongside the Ouse and Dee respectively. We owe our earliest man-made canal to the Romans: this is the Fossdyke, connecting Lincoln with the Trent at Torksey and still in use. In later centuries, further visitors such as the Vikings brought their long ships across the seas and began settling in the country around the larger rivers. They raided and plundered Ireland along the mighty Shannon and are said to have floated their craft over shallows in the River Lee to the north-east of London by constructing temporary weirs with their spears and shields to raise water levels—an early form of elementary flash lock.

Little systematic improvement of river navigations took place until the fifteenth century when works were carried out on the Thames, Lee and Yorkshire Ouse. These took the form of navigation weirs or flash locks (see below), generally constructed in association with mill weirs. Long-distance transport along such routes was an uncertain and time-consuming affair, with delays of days or weeks while water levels built up sufficiently to enable deep-draughted barges to negotiate shallows. There was considerable conflict between navigation and milling interests and the early history of our river highways is characterized by disputes between the rival factions.

With the opening of a short section of the canalized River Exe in Devon in 1572, a great leap forward was made possible by the building of pound locks where a short section of waterway was enclosed at each end by vertically rising gates. Similar devices were known in Holland at the end of the fourteenth century, while the resourceful Leonardo da Vinci (1452–1519) designed pound locks for the Duke of Milan with conventional mitre-gates of the type widely found on canals and rivers to the present day. Soon after the opening of the Exeter Canal, the first British lock with swinging gates appeared on the River Lee at Waltham Abbey. Throughout the seventeenth century river navigations flourished. Reminders of this period are the turf-sided locks of the River Wey in Surrey (below) and slightly later ones on the Berkshire River Kennet.

Greater progress was made in the building of artificial navigation canals on the Continent. Almost a century before the start of Britain's Canal Age, the French engineer Pierre-Paul Riquet connected the Atlantic with the Mediterranean with a one hundred and fifty mile canal between Toulouse and Sète. Known as the Canal du Midi, building lasted from 1666 to 1681. All the features

One of the earliest forms of inland craft was the dug-out canoe, formed from a single tree trunk. This fine example, thought to date from medieval times, was recovered from Thames mud at Shepperton, during dredging operations in the mid-1960s.

River navigations such as the Thames have been important trade routes since prehistoric times. Here, sailing barges and other small craft are seen passing Lambeth Palace, London, in 1709.

The man who started England's Canal Age: the Third Duke of Bridgewater, proudly displaying the Barton Aqueduct, which carried his navigation over the River Irwell, near Manchester.

of canals as we now know them were utilized: aqueducts, a tunnel and numerous locks with oval chambers. At Agde, there is a remarkable circular lock with three entrances.

Francis, Third Duke of Bridgewater, is generally credited with the building of Britain's first modern canal: certainly his navigation which enabled coal from the ducal mines at Worsley to be carried cheaply to Manchester caught the public imagination when its original length was opened in 1761. As a consequence, the succeeding seventy years saw the planning and execution of our waterways system as we know it now. But two decades before, eighteen miles of Newry Canal between the east coast of Ulster and Lough Neagh and featuring fourteen locks with a 50-ton barge capacity was constructed: it opened in 1742.

The Duke of Bridgewater's successful navigation, whereby the cost of transport plummeted, resulted from a fruitful partnership with his agent, John Gilbert, and a self-taught engineering genius named James Brindley. Although scarcely able to read or write, Brindley's previous experience as a millwright and surveyor proved invaluable. While his canal building work lasted for less than thirteen years, from 1759 to his death in 1772, his name is linked with many of the canals of the period.

These include a system connecting the four great river estuaries of England: the Thames, Mersey, Severn and Humber, meeting in the heart of the country, in Birmingham.

With a handful of exceptions where Government money was used, most of our canals were promoted by private enterprise, often as the result of wealthy landowners and businessmen pooling their resources to bring cheap and reliable transport to a locality. In one sense this piecemeal planning was eventually to be the death of waterways freight: no standard gauge was ever adopted for the canal structures, with individual companies selecting a size of lock and channel width that suited local rather than national requirements. While the standard narrow-gauge canals radiating from Birmingham admitted boats 70 ft long with a 7-ft beam, those of Yorkshire and the North East were intended for use by shorter craft such as the Humber keels. Thus, with length restrictions of between 58 ft and 62 ft, although sufficiently wide to accommodate a pair of narrow boats, their length prevented this. Numerous regional types of canal craft therefore evolved, unable to trade very far from their home waters. Even to present times, the existence of seventeen narrow locks at Watford and Foxton on the Grand Union's Leicester Section

James Brindley, the self-taught and brilliant engineer who was associated with many early canals in England until his death in 1772.

Birmingham Canal Navigations.

Received the Twenty sixth day of December 1836 from Ebenezer Johnston of Bishopsgate Street, Without in the City of London, Esquire

the sum of Seventy One Pounds, being the proportional sum allocated on One Subdivided Share, N.º 3343 in this Undertaking pursuant to the Company's Act passed in the 5.th Year of his Majesty King William the 4.th and of the Resolution of a Special Assembly of the Proprietors, held on the 18.th December, 1835.

£71.0.0

John Fawcett

Clerk to the said Company of Proprietors

prevents interchange of broad-beam boats between the wide waterways of the North and South. A pleasure cruiser able to travel everywhere on the connected network of England and Wales must not exceed about 46 ft × 6 ft 10 in. in beam.

While waterways like Thomas Telford's Birmingham and Liverpool Junction Canal (Shropshire Union), completed in 1835 in the final years of the Canal Era, were constructed by using bold engineering techniques—long, deep, straight cuttings and tall embankments—Britain's canals were almost entirely the work of manual labour. Picks and shovels, thousands of low-paid workers (navvies) travelling between one construction site and the next, and cheap local building materials are elements that are typical of this development in inland transport. Once money had been raised for a venture, an early completion date was imperative. Not infrequently, however, canals greatly exceeded their estimated finishing time and there is only one on record that was built for less than its planned cost. In spite of these beginnings, the more successful concerns enjoyed a period of very considerable prosperity. This lasted until the coming of the

A share certificate issued to one Ebenezer Johnston of London on 29 December 1836 for a stake in the Birmingham Canal Navigations. The purchase price was £71.

railways after 1825 and, in some instances, with forceful management for much of the remainder of the nineteenth century. By comparison, the mania for canals that gripped Britain during the 1790s saw money poured into all kinds of unlikely projects where hopes of satisfactory financial returns were never realized.

At its zenith in the middle of the last century, the waterways system provided many alternative routes, including three over the Pennines (only one now survives), a link from the South Coast to the Thames, several between Thames and Severn and lines that penetrated deep into Central Wales. Given a boat of suitable dimensions it was possible to travel direct between Littlehampton, Sussex and Ripon, Yorkshire. Or from Somerset to the Fens. For every isolated coastal navigation, there was, as often as not, a plan to make a connection with the main network. While Parliamentary powers were obtained for such works, an Act did not by any means guarantee construction being undertaken. One obvious addition to the map that was promoted but not achieved was a canal to join the River Stort, north of London, with the River Cam and the area served by the Great Ouse. Maps on page 19 show that while Ireland was well served by a connected waterways system, the hilly

The Canal Age produced many remarkable schemes for waterways and structures to overcome changes in level. This plan for a double inclined plane lift for tub boats was published in 1796. Motive power was provided by self-emptying buckets descending a well.

nature of Scotland was less conducive to canal building. Here, work was chiefly concentrated in the Midlands between Edinburgh and Glasgow, with the coast-to-coast Caledonian and Crinan Canals planned in isolation for convenience to sea-going vessels.

Of all canal structures, the lock is one that most interests the casual observer. During fine weather, there is no waterway lock in Britain with direct road access that does not have its group of by-standers for whom there is a slightly contemptuous term—'gongoozlers'. This was long ago defined as 'an idle and inquisitive person who stands staring for prolonged periods at anything out of the common'. The locks of one waterway vary from those of another in a number of respects, but the drawing on page 24 may be taken as typical of a wide beam such as is found on the Leeds and

Construction work in progress at Islington Tunnel on the Regent's Canal, London, in 1819.

Liverpool, Grand Union or Kennet and Avon Canals. A chamber of brick or stone impounds a short section of canal between mitre gates. Using the analogy of the domestic bath, water enters at the upper level by turning on 'taps', variously known as paddles, cloughs or racks. These normally take the form of sliding wooden shutters at the entrance to an underground culvert: they are wound open or shut by attaching a handle to the spindle of the paddle gear. Many top gates are also fitted with paddles, thus speeding up the operation. To empty the lock, the 'plug' is pulled out by opening paddles set either in the lower gates or on the banks. Only when the water level inside the chamber is equal to that in the canal outside, can the top or bottom gates be opened, generally by pushing on outstretched balance beams. For different systems based on the same theme, see the section on locks below. Larger locks on commercial waterways are often mechanized, with gate and paddle operations controlled by hydraulic machinery from a keeper's cabin or switch panel.

The Bridgewater Canal's Barton Aqueduct as it appeared in the late eighteenth century. It was replaced during the 1890s by the present Barton Swing Aqueduct, necessitated by construction of the Manchester Ship Canal.

The deepest lock in these islands is on the Shannon at Ardnacrusha Power Station, where twin chambers have a total lift of 110 ft. At the other end of the scale, some canal stop locks feature a change in levels of little more than 6 in.

To most people, a major interest of the inland waterways is the wealth of delightful domestic and industrial architecture evidenced by bridges, aqueducts, warehouses, pubs, houses and cottages. While the canals enabled the Industrial Revolution to become a reality by offering cheap transport of raw materials and finished goods, they were created in an age of elegance. Thus we have wonderful classical structures like the aqueducts of the Kennet and Avon or the office buildings of original canal companies. Even in its most simple form, canal design is pleasing, ever varied and functionally good to look at. Note the flowing lines of bridge parapets, where projections would snag a towing rope, or the patterns of courses of projecting ribbed brickwork on lock sides and the towpath through bridge holes to prevent boat horses slipping in wet weather. Canals were one of the last great works in Britain before the advent of mass production, consequently everything bears the unmistakable stamp of its designer.

Cast iron was one material that reached a new

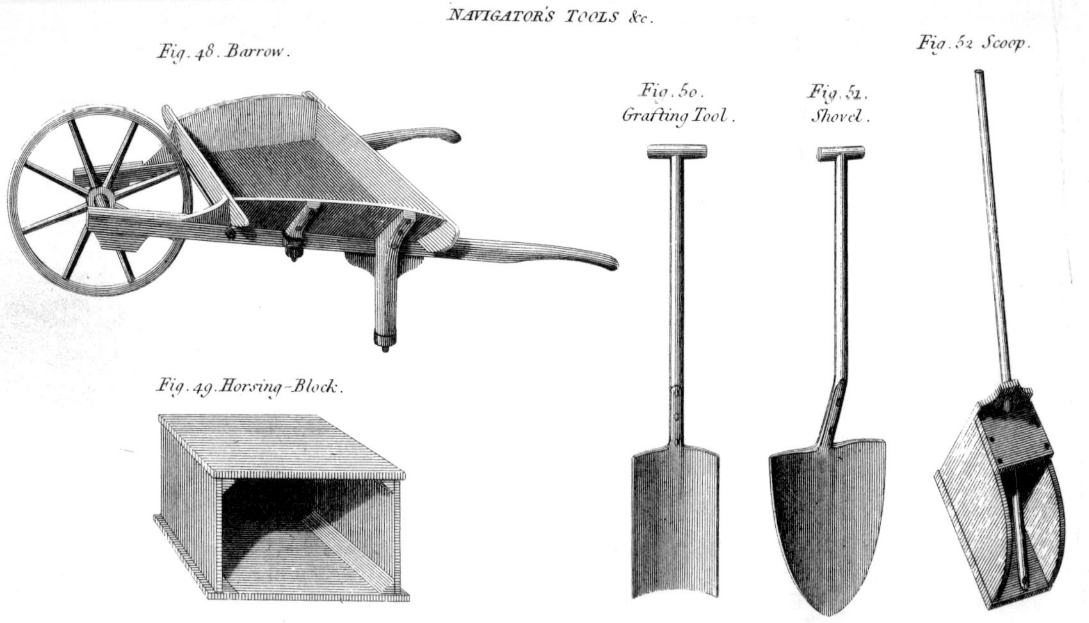

NAVIGATOR'S TOOLS &c.

Fig. 48. Barrow.

Fig. 50.
Grafting Tool.

Fig. 51.
Shovel.

Fig. 52 Scoop.

Fig. 49. Horsing-Block.

The great majority of British canals were dug with the most elementary tools. Here is a selection of devices used by the Navigators (Navvies is a term derived from the canal builders); the print was published in 1806.

The most usual method of making a canal bed watertight was to line it with 'puddle clay', a mixture of suitable loam and water, worked into position by the navvies' feet. Here the technique is being used for repairs to the Llangollen Canal in 1971.

popularity side by side with canal building. Thus it provides long-lasting items of equipment, from complete sectional bridges to mile plates, paddle gear, boundary markers and mooring bollards. Its widespread use by the later Victorians was apt to result in complicated and fussy ornament, but on the canals, cast iron can be seen in many bold and honest applications.

Our waterways are one of the richest sources of industrial archaeology. Since the 1960s, this heritage has been increasingly appreciated and structures that were decayed have, in many instances, been refurbished or returned to their original appearance.

For about seventy years until the 1840s, inland water transport flourished supreme. But the coming of the railways, steam power and a stubbornness by some canal companies to co-operate or modernize their works left the network something of a Cinderella among freight carriers. Quiet, efficient but undramatic, the waterways could not

The navigable waterways of England and Wales in 1974.

Left and far left
The waterways systems of Scotland and Ireland. Broken lines indicate sections that are no longer open to boats.

compete with the publicity-conscious Victorian railways. A number were bought up by railway companies to reduce the competition. Some were well run by their new owners; others, including the Kennet and Avon and Stratford Canals, were systematically starved of traffic by the Great Western Railway and by-laws introduced to prevent trading on Sundays. Maintenance would be neglected to the extent that owners could apply for legal sanctions to close down the line on the grounds of No Demand, when in fact boats were physically unable to load economic cargoes, so shallow was the channel.

Elsewhere, things were different. Some concerns like the Weaver Navigation in Cheshire, the Bridgewater Canal and the Aire and Calder were always making improvements, lengthening locks, providing deeper water or seeking new methods of carrying waterborne freight. (See the Tom Puddings below.)

In spite of general neglect in many areas, some waterways remained prosperous. In 1927, two years before creation of the Grand Union Canal

The late eighteenth and early nineteenth century canals display superbly well-designed examples of functional but attractive architecture. This is the staircase lock at Bratch, on the Staffordshire and Worcestershire Canal. The charming octagonal building is a toll collection house.

A detail of one of the arches of John Rennie's classical Dundas Aqueduct, constructed in Bath stone. Built in the very early nineteenth century, it conveys the Kennet and Avon Canal over the River Avon, several miles east of Bath, Somerset.

Hectic traffic on a waterway that escaped railway domination and has been constantly improved to carry increasing quantities of goods. This is the Aire and Calder Navigation at Ferrybridge Lock, Yorkshire, in 1895. The keel barges, drawn by horse or steam tug, appear to be delayed by construction work to increase the lock's capacity.

from several independent routes, this two hundred and forty mile system transported about 2·75 million tons of goods. In the same year, the Aire and Calder could boast 2·4 million tons, while the Leeds and Liverpool, one hundred and forty-two miles with its branches, achieved 1·8 million tons. One of the busiest sections this century was the one hundred and fifty-nine mile narrow locked Birmingham Canal Navigations, where a little over 4 million tons of cargo was recorded in 1927. It should not therefore be considered that Britain's canals were a total transport failure by the end of the last century.

After some evidence pointing to a possible revival in the 1930s, when the Grand Union Canal Co. doubled the capacity of many locks south of Birmingham, a large number of the old companies were nationalized in 1948. During the first five years of Government control, total tonnage carried annually increased from 11·2 million to 12·7 million. Various changes in title of the controlling body led to the formation of the British Waterways Board in 1963. Under the Transport Act of 1968, it was recognized that some waterways would never again play a significant part in transport, but that they had a very bright future ahead for all kinds of amenity. Another group was classified as

An early form of traction on rivers and certain canals was bow-hauling by gangs of men who were able to scramble along river beds and banks that were unsuitable for horses. The bow-hauliers were a notoriously rough and troublesome body of individuals. This scene is on the now disused Thames and Severn Canal in Gloucestershire.

commercial and these comprise the Aire and Calder, Calder and Hebble, Caledonian, Crinan, Sheffield and South Yorkshire, New Junction, Trent, Weaver, Severn, Gloucester, and Sharpness and Lee. Other independent routes that carry

(right)
Even a simple device like a lock by-pass weir can be a structure of beauty on the eighteenth-century Staffordshire and Worcestershire Canal. The iron cage is to prevent branches and other debris from passing into the underground culvert.

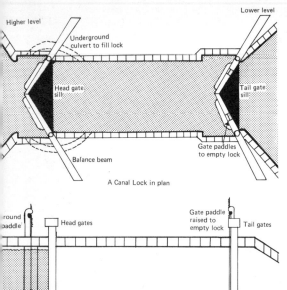

A Canal Lock in plan

A Canal Lock in cross-section

substantial amounts of traffic include the Yorkshire Ouse, the Lower Thames and, of course, the Manchester Ship Canal, the only completely new modern waterway in Britain since the end of the Canal Age.

Traffic over all British waterways in the 1970s is approaching 30 million tons a year: when compared with more than 240 million tons in Holland, over 235 million tons in Germany and 110 million in France, it can be appreciated that Britain has much ground to make up in developing this, the cheapest and most civilized form of bulk goods carriage known to man.

We are, none the less, on the threshold of important developments in the field of barge-carrying ships including LASH and BACAT (see below). There seem, at last, to be definite prospects of enlarging locks between Rotherham and Doncaster on the Sheffield and South Yorkshire Navigation to enable BACAT barges to trade efficiently between the English interior and the European Continent. And, during 1974, a feasibility study

Once very widespread over many English canals, the traditionally painted narrow boat continued to trade in significant numbers until the end of the 1960s. This view on the Grand Union Canal at Brentford, Middlesex, shows boats waiting to load and unload, their destinations being Wellingborough and Birmingham.

was being made of the Southern Grand Union Canal to test its suitability for conversion to an upgraded BACAT-gauge waterway linking London and the Thames with the lower end of the M1 motorway and thus avoiding much road congestion in the centre of the metropolis.

For many people, the aspect of waterways that most affects them directly is the newly discovered amenity use. Gone are the days of dereliction if commercial traffic has vanished and now several million enthusiasts or holiday-makers enjoy themselves afloat at some time in each year. Disused canals that have been choked with weeds and trees for decades are being brought back to a useful and attractive life: lock gates are renewed, boating facilities provided and a scene of urban or rural squalor is replaced by one of beauty. Local authorities, the navigation bodies and volunteer workers combine in their efforts to improve and restore waterways. The latest success is a section of the outstandingly attractive Montgomeryshire Canal connecting mid-Wales with the Shropshire Union Main Line. This is to be reopened with

A modern and highly successful method of moving large quantities of coal between waterside pits and Ferrybridge Power Station, Yorkshire, via the Aire and Calder Navigation. Watched by the Castleford lock keeper, a Cawoods-Hargreaves compartment boat train heads for Ferrybridge in 1973. See left.

The decline of many smaller British canals as a transport medium coincided with their 'discovery' for pleasure cruising. Less than a day's boating distance from the heart of the Potteries, this lovely countryside awaits the explorer of the Trent and Mersey Canal's Caldon and Leek branches.

the aid and intervention of the Prince of Wales.

Inland waterways offer scope for all kinds of boating activity, which at one level or another is readily available to everyone. From canoe-camping to holidays in hired narrow-boat conversions, there are an ever-increasing number of people discovering a Britain that has changed little since the horse and cart era. Even the most prosaic industrial towns look newly interesting from the deck of a cruiser and there is a real fascination in gliding through a great city like Birmingham or London in surroundings that are often unexpectedly rural. But by far the majority of our waterways wind through peaceful meadows, across rugged stone-walled moorland or dive into the green canopy that overhangs a deep and dripping cutting through solid rock. Scotland's Caledonian Canal offers the most dramatic scenery, with a passage of Loch Ness and views of Ben Nevis at the Fort William end. For real and haunting isolation, go to Ireland to cruise on the Shannon, Grand Canal or Barrow Navigation, or northwards to Ulster's little-known Lakeland, where Upper and Lower Lough Erne are studded with wooded islands and offer a greater water area than Loch Lomond, the English Lake District and the Norfolk Broads combined.

The recreations that can be enjoyed on or beside

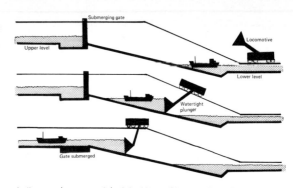

A diagram (not to scale) of the Water Slope or 'Push Puddle' lock, a latter twentieth-century answer to the problem of overcoming changes in level on canals. The first working example, at Montech on the Garonne Lateral Canal in France, was completed in 1973 and is the likely forerunner of further similar systems: 1,000-hp locomotives each side of a sloping gutter push a wedge-shaped quantity of water up the incline; when it nears the upper level, a gate submerges to the canal bed. The Montech Slope is 539 m. long, raises barges of 350 tons' capacity some 14 m. in about ten minutes, and, unlike conventional locks, wastes no water during the operation.

inland waterways include many forms of low-powered boating (with power-boat racing and water ski-ing in carefully selected areas where conflict with other users cannot develop); fishing; rambling; nature study; and often, most pleasant of all, gongoozling.

There really is no more pleasant way to travel long distances than by boat, beginning the day in one county, stopping for lunch in another and returning to within a few miles of the starting point in spite of six or seven hours of steady 4 mph of progress. Canals seem to go everywhere: there are connections with most parts of England; yet in another sense they often go nowhere in particular and the most beautiful length may terminate in a dead end. If you cover much more than one hundred miles during the course of a week, you could rightly be accused of unnecessary hurrying. Much greater distances are possible but are quite foreign to the spirit and object of this most relaxing occupation.

However briefly, mention must be made of canals and rivers abroad. The great majority are used for commercial transport side by side with pleasure boating in varying amounts. The Soviet Union has about 80,000 miles; the United States 25,000 miles in freight use. France offers 4,720 miles and Holland 4,600 miles. Unlike in Britain, constant enlargement, modernization, replacement of flights of locks by lifts or water slopes and upgrading to a European barge standard of 1,350 tons capacity are quite normal.

For the tourist, there are opportunities to explore most areas from aboard travelling hotel boats. A development that is especially growing in France is the operation of fleets of hire cruisers, enabling family parties to enjoy cruising while also taking a foreign holiday. With the exception of Holland and some of the trans-Atlantic waterways, boating facilities are not normally as well developed as in the British Isles, so a Continental cruise tends to be a slightly more adventurous undertaking than a week on the Thames or Norfolk Broads. But if you want to experience rivers and canals that teem with traffic and share a little of the excitement that is generated by the concept of barges whose journeys might range throughout Western Europe, the waterways across the English Channel have much to offer.

Hugh McKnight
The Clock House
Shepperton-on-Thames
1974

West Country Barge

During the eighteenth and early nineteenth centuries, traffic on the Upper Thames consisted of broad-beam wooden barges hauled from the towpath by teams of up to six horses or by gangs of men. A square-rigged sail would be hoisted when wind conditions were favourable. Journeys would sometimes take a number of weeks in times of drought or flood, and obstacles to progress included time-wasting flash locks. This engraving by R. and D. Havell was published in 1811 and shows the river at Maidenhead, Berks.

Wey Barge

One of the longest surviving timber-built canal barges, this craft continued in operation carrying grain between London Docks and the Wey Navigation at Coxes Mill Lock, Surrey, until 1969. The example shown, *Diligent*, was built at the Guildford yard of William Stevens and Sons in 1940, exactly a century after the Stevens family, owners of the Wey, began their barge traffic. Capable of carrying loads of 80 tons, the Wey barges had a beam of 13 ft 10½ in. The great rudder was designed to fold back against the hull when negotiating locks. During the last years of their service, they were hauled from London to Weybridge by tug and thereafter were frequently bow-hauled or poled to their destination up the Wey. The last of the Stevenses' barge horses stopped working in 1960. Several Wey barges are preserved, converted into spacious residential craft.

Narrow-Boat Steamer COUNT

The earliest form of powered narrow boat was the steamer, first introduced by the Grand Junction Canal Co. in 1864 (steam tugs had hauled dumb canal boats for a number of years beforehand). During the 1870s, Fellows, Morton and Clayton Ltd commenced carrying with steamers, chiefly on the Grand Union Canal between London and Braunston and along the Leicester Section to the Trent. The boats were equipped with counter sterns, like the modern narrow boat, iron sides and elm bottom planks. Living accommodation and space for the engine and coal-fired boiler reduced cargo capacity to about 20 tons compared with the 30 tons of the horse-drawn narrow boat. The last FMC steamer in service was converted to diesel propulsion in 1932. The steam engine shown here was built by FMC at their Saltley, Birmingham yard for narrow boat *Admiral* in 1905.

Horse-Drawn Narrow Boat (*left*)

The best-known type of canal craft is the narrow boat, designed to pass through locks measuring about 74 ft × 7 ft 2 in. Such narrow-gauge networks radiate from Birmingham and the Black Country and reach to Lancashire, the Severn, the Upper Thames and the East Midlands. Narrow boats were thus widely distributed on the canals as well as connecting river navigations. From about the middle of the last century, these craft were generally operated by families living aboard and the colourful decoration for which they are noted dates from that time. This example is from the fleet of the Shropshire Union Railways and Canal Co., a concern that ran boats on its own waterways until 1921 when their two hundred and two vessels were sold to other carriers. With the introduction of steam and, subsequently, diesel propulsion, horse boats were either used as unpowered 'butties' to motorized craft or, alternatively, were adapted to take engines. Especially with Number Ones (owner-operators), horse boats continued in service in small numbers until after World War II. During the 1970s, a single example remains in trade in the Birmingham area.

Steam Engine and Boiler, 1909

Shortly before the advent of the first semi-diesel engines for narrow boats, Messrs T. A. Savery and Co. developed a high-speed 20-hp steam engine with high-pressure water-tube boiler for their craft *Thistle*. This had the distinction of being provided with wheel steering forward of the engine room, instead of a conventional tiller on the stern. No living cabin was fitted.

Narrow-Boat Pair (*left*)

From the end of the first decade of the twentieth century until the present day, narrow-boat transport has been carried out mainly by pairs of craft. The unladen examples shown here are motor boat *Ian*, left, breasted up with her butty (unpowered), *Lucy*. Best adapted to wide-beam routes like the Grand Union, but also trading over narrow canals, these vessels were operated by Blue Line Canal Carriers Ltd until 1970, bringing coal from the Coventry Canal to Southall, Middlesex. Both were built in timber at Nurser's Braunston Dock, near Rugby.

Narrow-Boat People

The canal population has always been as much a source of interest as the colourful craft in which they made their homes. Often, several generations of the same family would follow this travelling way of life, acquiring great skills in boat handling and the techniques of making a living on the waterways. With their own pubs, schools, shops and welfare services, the narrow-boat people mixed little with 'folk off the land' and remained a close-knit, self-sufficient community until the virtual demise of traffic in the 1960s. Seen in the cabin of her British Waterways butty is Mrs Tom Humphries.

Narrow-Boat People

In 1881, it was estimated that there were about forty thousand children of school age living on canal boats. In spite of legislation, few of them received much formal education. Even in recent years, narrow-boat children attended school only at infrequent intervals, but this in no way dulled their natural intelligence. Photographed in 1961 are Janet, Colin and Muriel Harris, whose parents worked a pair of craft for the Willow Wren Company.

Narrow-Boat People

While there are now no longer any of the old canal families earning their full-time living from narrow boats, various craft continue to trade from time to time, manned by a new generation of canal enthusiasts. Often, they deliver cargoes such as coal or lime juice from Brentford to Boxmoor on the Grand Union Canal, drawing an income from other occupations as well. This pair of Foxton Boat Services craft are hired out as camping pleasure boats in the summer. When the holiday season is over, Tony Clark and Bryan Allen enjoy some real commercial boating. They are pictured here with a load of stone brought from Peterborough to the Grand Union Canal at Bulbourne, where it was used for bank repairs, October 1973.

Narrow-Boat Decoration

One of Britain's last surviving folk arts, the unique painting of narrow boats continues to flourish more than one hundred years after it was first recorded in *Household Words*, a magazine edited by Charles Dickens. We can only guess at the origins of the colourful flowers, castle pictures and geometrical designs. Although some boatmen were adept at applying their own painting, most was undertaken at boatyards scattered throughout the network. Although certain conventions are adhered to, there are definite regional variations, enabling an expert to distinguish between work from, for example, the Potteries, the Birmingham area and Braunston. Apart from the exterior surfaces of the boats, items of equipment such as water cans, dippers and stools were covered with decorations. Lettering, as on this cabin side of tar-carrying boat *Umea*, is bold and heavily shaded. Note the brass-bound chimney, with water can alongside.

Narrow-Boat Roses

While a variety of flowers are featured in the designs of these craft, roses predominate. Strong primary colours are used to apply petals over a blob of background paint. All the work is executed freehand and remarkably quickly. The circle of roses is a rather unusual example, applied to the combed wood-grain finish of a cabin bulkhead. In complete contrast, the very realistic spray of flowers on a cabin door is in the 'Knobstick' style, associated with the Trent and Mersey Canal around the Potteries.

Narrow-Boat Castles

Essential elements of a castle scene are a lake at the foot of a range of mountains with a foreground bridge that is certainly inspired by those hump-backed structures widely seen on the canals.

Left A cupboard door, hinged along its lower edge to form a table when opened.

Below left This panel from a Polesworth yard on the Coventry Canal was prepared as a 'pattern' for the guidance of apprentice painters.

Below Few flat surfaces escaped decoration on the better-maintained boats. Here, a cabin block supports the after end of the top planks which extend the length of the cargo space, providing a framework enabling the hold to be covered with waterproof sheets.

Ropework

The well-turned-out narrow boat features a number of ropework items, some functional and decorative, others purely decorative. The most obviously useful examples are the plaited fenders generally found on fore-end and stern: these protect the boats themselves and also save lock gates and other canal installations from damage. Techniques are adapted from maritime traditions for the most part as can be seen from the 'Ram's Head', or rudder, of the British Waterways butty in the picture. Interwoven belts around the rudder top and the tiller are three-part 'Turk's Heads'. The elegant device down the back of the rudder is appropriately called a 'Swan's Neck'. Spherical fender is known as a 'Tipcat'. Many of the boat people were adept at making these designs themselves and scrubbed them frequently to preserve a well-cared-for appearance. The photograph was taken at the Bull's Bridge layby, on the Grand Union Canal at Southall, Middlesex, in 1965.

Boat Building

A view of the important Fellows, Morton and Clayton narrow-boat dock at Saltley, Birmingham, about 1900. There were scores of building and repair yards throughout the narrow-boat waterways: most were quite small concerns, unlike FMC who obviously operated a sizeable production line. New craft were generally built on a side-slip, like that shown here, and launched down greased tracks, parallel with the canal. Alternatively, a dry dock would be used that could be flooded when the boat was ready to have fitting out completed afloat, in the foreground, the wooden keel and elm bottom planks of one craft have been laid, prior to adding the sides of the hull in either timber or iron. Similar techniques are still used at many modern pleasure-cruiser firms, where narrow boats are normally built in steel.

Grand Union Canal Wide Boat

Although built to accommodate 14-ft-wide barges from London to Braunston, the Grand Union Canal's chief long-distance traffic was in pairs of narrow boats which could more easily travel through the waterway's somewhat limited cross-section. Furthermore, their use did not require one-way working of the two long tunnels at Blisworth and Braunston. However, widening of the Braunston to Birmingham section during the 1930s did encourage the building of two experimental diesel-powered wide boats, with a beam of about 12 ft 6 in. and capacity of 66 tons. It was intended that they should tow butties of similar dimensions. One, *Progress*, was made by Bushell Bros at their Tring yard for the Grand Union Canal Carrying Co.; the other was commissioned by Fellows, Morton and Clayton Ltd. Named *Pioneer*, she is seen here at the firm's Uxbridge yard shortly after launching. For the reasons given above, neither was a great success. *Progress* was used for a number of years on maintenance work and is now a converted mobile houseboat.

Thames Sailing Barges

Of all the different regional types of flat-bottomed sailing barge, those of the Thames and Medway are the best known. Home waters were the rivers and coastal creeks of South-East England. Very seaworthy, yet exceptionally manoeuvrable even in confined areas like the Pool of London, some were equipped with auxiliary engines in later years. Capacity varied from 50 to 150 tons. with an average of around 120. The smallest type was particularly well suited to travelling up the Regent's Canal from Limehouse. Sadly, these magnificent boats with billowing tan sails are no longer one of the sights of London River, for the last to trade by sail alone, *Cambria*, was retired in 1970. Numbers declined from about two thousand and ninety in 1885 to about five hundred in 1939. Many live on as working pleasure craft, privately owned or sometimes available on charter. One, shown here, is *May*, 57 registered tons, built at Ipswich in 1891. She was first across the finishing line in the 1973 Greenwich Festival Smack and Sailing Barge Match.

Severn Trows

The Severn Estuary and Bristol Channel produced a distinctive sailing barge with a D-shaped stern known as the trow. Derived from square-rigged vessels that probably originated in the fifteenth century, they were mostly fitted with a fore and aft rig by the middle of the last century. Those exclusively used on the Severn and around the West Country coasts were about 70 ft long with a beam of 17 ft; others capable of entering the Droitwich, Stroudwater and Kennet and Avon Canals were rather smaller. That illustrated, *Barbara of Gloster*, is seen at a village wharf in about 1897. As she lacks sailing gear, she was probably used mainly on the canals and Upper Severn.

Horse-Drawn Keel (*left*)

The Calder and Hebble Navigation wooden keel, *Thomas*, seen in about 1920. Built on similar lines to the sailing keels of the Humber area, they were between 57 ft 6 in. and 58 ft in length, with a beam of slightly more than 14 ft. Maximum load varied between 80 and 100 tons. Steel craft that are direct descendants of the horse-drawn keels, but powered by a diesel engine, can still be seen trading on the C. and H., Sheffield and South Yorkshire Navigation and connecting routes. The largest fleet, of about seventy vessels, is owned by Messrs E. V. Waddington of Swinton, near Mexborough.

Humber Keels

Otherwise known as Yorkshire keels, these craft were widely used over waterways of the North East, either horse-drawn or fitted with a huge square mainsail and topsail. Normal length was about 58 ft with a beam of about 14 ft 6 in. and capacity of between 80 and 100 tons. In spite of their size, they could be handled by a man working on his own, but were quite frequently operated by a family spending most of their life aboard. In about 1900, there were something like one hundred and fifty sailing keels using the River Ouse to the port of York alone. Keels continued in trade under sail until the last was withdrawn about 1949.

Norfolk Wherries

The working boat of the Norfolk and Suffolk Broads, the wherry was constructed of clinker oak planks and could load between 12 and 83 tons of cargo, depending on size. A single black gaff sail, without any boom, could readily be lowered when passing under bridges. Although sails were used on the narrowest sections of winding rivers like the Ant, if the wind was not favourable, the crews would pole these barges with long shafts terminating in a wooden disc and known as 'quants'. Much of the wherry trade was to and from the seaports at Lowestoft and Yarmouth. This 1890 scene shows a pair in Yarmouth Harbour, leaving with cargoes for the Broads.

Mersey Flats

A scale model of Mersey Flat *Pilot*, from Liverpool Museum. The original was built in 1894. The Mersey Flat was between 68 ft and 70 ft × 14 ft 3 in. to 14 ft 9 in. beam, loading up to 80 tons of cargo. Normal rig was a gaff mainsail with foresail. Considerably larger were the closely related Weaver flats of around 90 ft × 21 ft beam and able to carry as much as 250 tons. As well as sailing versions, both types were to be found as dumb craft for horse or tug haulage, and later motorized, with first steam and finally diesel engines. Examples of flats could be found throughout the broad-beam rivers and canals of the North West. The sailing flats had all disappeared by the end of the last war, but various motorized or dumb derivatives can be found to this day.

Horse-Drawn Short Boat

Wide-beam locks of the Leeds and Liverpool Canal were constructed 10 ft shorter than those of the normal narrow-boat canals, necessitating use of a special breed of 'short boat', 62 ft long × 14 ft 3 in. beam and drawing about 3 ft 9 in. when loaded with a cargo of 45 to 50 tons. Cabins flush with the decks were provided bow and stern. All were horse-drawn until the arrival of steamers in the 1880s. This example shows *Ellen* of Wigan and *Connie*, both built in timber, waiting to ascend locks at the junction of the L. and L. main line and its Walton Summit Branch in May 1895.

Short-Boat Decoration

Less well known than the painted narrow boats, the designs of short boats featured elaborate shaded lettering, baroque scrolls and a variety of motifs including birds, flowers, fruit, animals and landscapes. When the square transom of the horse boats disappeared, a broad expanse admirably suited to decoration was lost. There-

after, the upper planks of the rounded sterns and the bluff bows offered a more restricted scope for embellishment. Generally, a short-boat painting has greater links with maritime traditions than that of the narrow boats. There are also undeniable similarities with the work of the fairground sign writer.

Short-Boat Steamer

Steam engines were first fitted to Leeds and Liverpool Canal short boats in the 1880s and a regular day and night flyboat service was introduced along the one hundred and twenty-seven mile Leeds–Liverpool route. Living accommodation on these craft was confined to a cabin in the bows, for the engine and boiler occupied available space at the stern. Generally working on a motor and butty system like the narrow-boat pairs (a powered vessel towing an unpowered one), the steamers were frequently manned by families living aboard. Engines were normally tandem V-form, exhausting to atmosphere. They continued to be built until the 1930s, by which time diesel units had taken over. This picture, dating from the early 1950s, shows one of the last at work, with a coal cargo of about 50 tons.

Diesel Short Boats

Traffic on the Leeds and Liverpool Canal at Aintree, during the late 1950s. *Progress*, foreground, is a typical diesel-powered short boat with an unpowered butty being towed through the railway bridge. Alongside is a laden butty, whose motor is just disappearing out of sight. Engines included Nationals, Gardners, Listers and Widdops, locally built at Keighley, Yorkshire. All hulls seen here are timber, although iron and steel were used from the 1930s, notably with a small fleet constructed by British Waterways in 1950 and 1952. The last regular short-boat traffic, carrying coal to Wigan Power Station along the Leigh Branch from the Bridgewater Canal, ceased in 1972. These vessels may still be seen on maintenance duty, and Mr John Liley's famous *Arthur* crossed the English Channel in 1972 to make an extensive tour of Continental waterways.

Bridgewater Steam Tugs

The Bridgewater Department of the Manchester Ship Canal Co. operated a fleet of powerful steam tugs during the first three decades of the twentieth century. Built with similar dimensions to narrow boats, they were fitted with wheel steering and crew accommodation in the stern. Major use was in hauling flats and other unpowered barges along the Bridgewater Canal. This view on the canal at Runcorn, Cheshire, dates from about 1910.

Narrow-Beam Canal Tug

Built on the Thames and Severn Canal in 1908 at the works of Messrs Abdela and Mitchell Ltd, *Sharpness* was one of several similar craft designed for use on the Severn, and Worcester and Birmingham Canal. The hull was of galvanized steel, 45 ft long with a draught of about 4 ft. The 30-hp petrol/paraffin engine drove a four-bladed propeller. Duties included towing horse boats through Tardebigge and Shortwood Tunnels, and breaking ice. She is now in private ownership as a cruiser and can frequently be seen moored on the Lower Avon Navigation in Worcestershire, with exterior little changed from its original appearance. The picture was taken in 1908.

Weaver Steam Flat

One of the great timber-built steam flats that traded under the flag of the Salt Union, formed in 1888 from a number of Cheshire and Worcestershire salt producers. 90 ft long with a beam of 21 ft, a full cargo totalled about 250 tons. Construction methods were similar to the sailing flats used in this part of the North West. A rope trailing from the stern suggests that an unpowered flat is in tow. The picture was taken on the Weaver Navigation at Vale Royal, in about 1908.

London Canal Tug

Much of the commercial traffic of London waterways (the Lee Navigation, Regent's Canal and lower Grand Union) has always been carried in wide-beam dumb barges. Steam tugs were introduced on the Regent's Canal in 1855, when single horse barges could be assembled into trains. In due course, such tugs were replaced by diesel-propelled craft, such as that shown here, built in the 1930s. The V-shaped steel hull closely resembled larger tugs at work in the Port of London. Note the massive rope fender on the bows, enabling barges to be pushed into a suitable position for towing. *Swallow* was photographed in 1947, and craft of the type can still be found at work in the area. The ramp in the background enabled barge horses to be led back to the towpath if they fell in the water.

Irish Canal Barge

96E is a Grand Canal maintenance barge, designed to fit the locks of the canal system between Dublin and the Shannon. First horse-hauled barges were of timber, but after 1925 steel hulls were constructed, forty-nine being launched up to 1939. The normal engine is a single-cylinder 16-hp Bolinder, heavy and reliable, with an irregular exhaust note. Trading ceased in 1960, but a number of the boats are still to be found on maintenance work. Provided with numbers rather than names, the suffix 'E' denotes an engineering function. Among cargo craft, 'M' indicated a Company-owned motor boat and 'B' stood for bye-trader, or the hack boats of a private operator. The Government commissioned twenty-nine wooden horse boats during World War II, to carry turf to power stations: these were distinguished by the letter 'G'.

Scottish Herring Boat

With a maximum vessel limit of 500 tons, the major commercial traffic of Scotland's 60-mile Caledonian Canal is sturdy fishing vessels. They follow the herring shoals from the North Sea to the Atlantic, saving considerable time and effort by means of the 12-hour canal passage. Here, timber-built *Faithful* descends the staircase of four Muirtown Locks at Inverness, at the eastern end of the waterway in 1972.

Tom Puddings

Otherwise known as 'pans' or 'compartment boats', this ingenious system of hauling long trains of coal boats on the Aire and Calder Navigation in Yorkshire was patented by the company's engineer, W. H. Bartholomew, in 1862. Initially moved by steam-powered push tug (the first-ever use of push tugs, now widely used on major inland waterways in the United States and elsewhere), Tom Puddings are today pulled by diesel tug, a train sometimes consisting of fifteen or more compartments, each loading 35 tons of coal. The square containers are attached to each other by means of chains and are loaded at chutes supplied with coal by either railway trucks or lorries. On reaching their destination at Goole Docks, they pass into an elevator and are inverted, so that the cargo can be poured direct into the hold of a sea-going collier.

Ferrybridge Compartment Barges

During the 1960s, the principle of the century-old Tom Pudding boats was adopted by two leading Yorkshire barge firms, Messrs Cawoods and Messrs Hargreaves. Trains of three 210-ton capacity barges, moved by push tug, are loaded at various collieries and moved down the Aire and Calder Navigation to Ferrybridge C Power Station. Here, they are shunted beneath a 'barge tippler', lifted 40ft above the water on a cradle, and inverted so that the coal pours down a chute. The operation is completed in nine minutes, resulting in a handling capacity at Ferrybridge of 1,000 tons per hour. The picture shows two empty barges passing Hargreaves' Castleford Dock, where two more units lie in a side basin.

Severn Oil Tanker

Coasting oil tankers navigated the upper reaches of the River Severn to Worcester and Stourport until the late 1960s. Development of overland pipelines then brought about a decline in commercial traffic on the waterway. This example from the Harker fleet was pictured in Tewkesbury Lock in 1967.

Trent Barge (*right*)

Steel-hulled diesel barges are still frequent users of the North Eastern waterways, coming far inland up the Trent to Gainsborough, Newark and Nottingham. In former years, such traffic was handled by sailing keels. The vessel shown is one of the British Waterways general merchandise fleet, *Kappa*, negotiating a bend in the tidal Trent at Owston Ferry. The river can handle barges up to 400 tons' carrying capacity.

BACAT

A new and exciting opportunity for intensive commercial traffic on the waterways of Yorkshire and the North East has been provided by the invention of BACAT craft—Barges Aboard CATamaran. These units measure 55 ft × 15 ft and carry a maximum load of 140 tons on a draught of 8 ft 1 in. They are close-coupled in trains of three, powered by a push tug which can also pull. The vessel shown is *Freight Pioneer*, one of two introduced by the British Waterways Board, and photographed on the Sheffield and South Yorkshire Navigation above Doncaster Lock in 1972. With the successful completion of the first Danish BACAT ship, late in 1973, eighteen barges can be transported between British ports and the Continent, via Rotterdam. On arrival in Europe, they are unloaded by the ship's built-in lifting apparatus, to continue their journey by inland waterway. If required, the BACAT ship can carry ten BACAT barges and three LASH lighters. Of catamaran design, each ship measures 103·5 m × 20·7 m with a draught of 5·4 m.

LASH

An American system of barge-carrying ships (Lighter Aboard SHip), there were twenty-two in operation or being built at the end of 1973. Two, *Acadia Forest* and *Atlantic Forest*, are now in service on a fortnightly run between New Orleans, Sheerness in the Medway Estuary,

Rotterdam and Bremerhaven. According to size, each ship carries from seventy-three to eighty-nine lighters measuring 61 ft 6 in. × 31 ft 2 in. on an 8 ft 8 in. draught with 435 tons loaded. For inland waterway use, the lighters are linked together for push or pull towing. To be lifted aboard the mother

ship, they are marshalled to a dock at the stern and picked up by a crane travelling on rails from the stern to a point near the bows, where the bridge and crews' quarters are located. The photograph opposite shows a single lighter being moved into position for loading aboard *Acadia Forest* in the Medway, 1970.

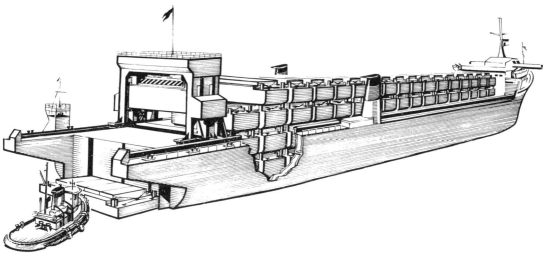

Horse-Drawn Ice Breaker

The greatest threat to canal traffic is ice. In former years, all the navigation companies operated ice breakers similar to this example seen at work on the Birmingham Canal Navigations at Wednesfield in 1954. The hull was either of stout iron or heavy timber construction, sheathed with iron plates to prevent the ice cutting into the planking. With fine lines and an acutely pointed bow, the round-bilged boat would be violently rocked from side to side by a gang of men standing on a central wooden platform, gripping a bar or taut rope. Teams of horses (sometimes as many as a dozen, in exceptionally severe weather) hauled the ice breaker, as it noisily crashed along the canal, leaving a clear passage for cargo craft in its wake. Steam- and diesel-powered versions were also in use.

Spoon Dredger

One of the most important tasks of canal maintenance is to preserve a good depth of water and so prevent boats grounding on the bottom. Silt and other refuse washed into the waterway must periodically be removed. The most basic type of dredger consists of a manually operated scoop, like that shown fitted to a Birmingham Canal Navigations narrow boat and seen operating at Salford Junction in about 1910. The iron spoon, attached to a wooden arm, is pushed along the canal bed, and then wound to the surface by operating a small crane. Spoil is then either transferred to the dredger boat or another mud hopper tied alongside. A three-man gang could recover up to 25 tons in a working day. More sophisticated methods of mechanical dredging using steam or diesel power were subsequently adopted.

Steam Drag Dredger

Almost certainly the oldest working steam boat in the world is this extraordinary dredger from Bridgwater Dock, Somerset, terminus of the Bridgwater and Taunton Canal. A brass plaque on the engine records that it was constructed by 'Geo. Lunel & Co., Engineers, Bristol. 1844'. It is generally considered that the designer was Isambard Kingdom Brunel, noted for his steam ships like the *Great Britain*. After one hundred and twenty seven years of operation at Bridgwater, the boat was taken overland to be preserved afloat at the Exeter Maritime Museum in 1971. Chains are attached to the side of the canal and are wound round a steam-driven drum: in this way the boat is hauled across the waterway, and mud is pushed to the sides by means of a blade beneath the stern. The blade can be raised vertically clear of the canal bottom for a return journey. Note the large iron flywheel on the left.

Steam Unloading Plants

The Grand Junction Canal Co. was one of many waterway authorities which acquired steam-powered grab dredgers, either mounted aboard boats or as in this case used on the canal bank for unloading mud from hoppers. Towing from one site to another would normally be by steam traction engine. The pair illustrated were photographed on the Leicester Section at Yelvertoft in 1896, where they were disposing of mud recovered at a nearby site by the Company's floating steam grabs *Waterway* and *Navigation*. Canal dredgers most commonly used today are diesel-powered: either land-based drag-line cranes or one of several kinds which can be floated from site to site.

Work Flats

The maintenance ganger's floating workshop is usually a simple rectangular punt of timber or steel construction. Tools and equipment can be stored in a small lock-up cabin at the stern which also provides shelter and a wood stove where tea can be brewed. The hold is sufficiently large to carry several tons of clay 'puddle' for bank repairs, items of lock equipment, or other materials that may be required for the work in question. The true canal work flat is not generally powered, but is propelled by horse or man on the towpath, or towed behind a motorized maintenance vessel. Flats can always be found at the scene of lock stoppages, where repairs are in progress. That shown here, *Fly*, was built for use on the Wey Navigation in Surrey.

Bucket Chain Dredger

Heavy-duty dredging on rivers and other larger water-ways is most commonly achieved by means of the curious diesel-driven device shown here. An endless chain of steel buckets or scoops is dragged across the bed of the navigation, once the craft has been secured to the chosen spot by chains or wire ropes. When they reach the top of the elevator, the buckets are inverted, spilling their contents into a chute that passes directly to a hopper barge moored alongside. This example was seen on the Rhône–Sête Canal in Southern France, in 1973.

Victorian Pleasure Craft

An advertisement, published in the 1880s, and promoting the products of a leading builder of small pleasure boats. Many similar firms operated on the Thames and other rivers, bringing great craftmanship to the construction of skiffs, rowing dinghies, punts and canoes. Since World War II, the small-boat industry has largely moved over to glass-reinforced plastic, and motor cruisers find customers more readily than traditional unpowered craft.

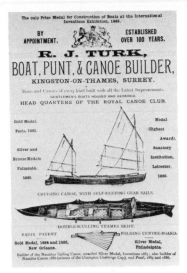

Victorian Pleasure Steamers
(*right*)

The late Victorian and Edwardian era saw the coming of numerous excursion steamers on both rivers and canals. Church and school groups would enjoy outings aboard craft like *La Marguerite*, pausing here in a Thames lock while all eyes looked towards the photographer. Strangely, the railways, which had sounded the death-knell of boat services intended as a means of travelling from one place to another, made possible the Sunday excursion. Town dwellers could rapidly reach an embarkation point in the country. Salter Bros of Oxford began a regular run between Kingston and Oxford in the 1880s. The two-day trip remained until 1973, when Thames lock congestion had reached proportions that seriously disrupted advertised time-keeping.

Packet Boats

Until competition from the railways killed off a lucrative source of revenue, passenger craft were widely used over most British rivers and canals. The boats were of light construction with fine lines and drawn by frequently changed teams of horses. Speeds of up to 12 mph were sometimes maintained, with tickets available at various prices in three classes. Refreshments would be available *en route*, while one service on the Kennet and Avon Canal between Bath and Bradford-on-Avon offered entertainment by a string band. This picture shows the Liverpool Packet in 1802. Including scheduled halts, the 35-mile journey was completed in about eight hours. Such services were still running on Ireland's Grand Canal until as late as the 1840s, but by this time packet boats elsewhere were used mainly for pleasure travel.

Edwardian Canal-Boat Outing

If purpose-built tripping craft like the steamer above were not available, ordinary freight boats would often be pressed into service to provide summertime canal outings. The Salvation Army was responsible for organizing the day excursion shown at its start aboard horse-drawn keel barge *Edward* in 1911. A return journey of 15 miles from Elland to Shepley Bridge on the Calder and Hebble Navigation in Yorkshire was successfully completed. The bewhiskered skipper seen standing near the stern is Captain Claxton.

Steam Inspection Launch

Pleasure boats for river use reached a peak of perfection in the latter years of the nineteenth century, when steam launches were built of teak and mahogany, with fittings in shining brass. Always a luxury status symbol akin to the Rolls-Royce, they were available only to the wealthy. This magnificent boat, *Donola*, 53 ft long, was made by the Kingdon Yacht and Launch Engineering Company of Teddington, Middlesex, in 1893. Her engine was by de Vine of Chertsey. Originally in private ownership, she was acquired by the Thames Conservancy in 1920 and spent the next forty-eight years as an inspection launch in which Conservators made an annual tour of the river. Always maintained in pristine condition, she completed her final journey down the Thames to Greenwich in May 1969, before going into preservation at the National Maritime Museum. There are now about one hundred small steam launches in use on the waterways of Britain.

Steam Canal Cruiser

Apart from Company inspection craft, some of the first private powered canal cruisers were built for Henry Rodolph de Salis, a director of the narrow-boat carriers, Fellows, Morton and Clayton Ltd, and a widely travelled waterways enthusiast. Little is known about the boat illustrated, except that she was called *Dragon Fly*, was narrow beam and was built on the Upper Thames in the late 1880s. At about 30 ft overall, she was presumably too small for de Salis' purposes, for a 59-ft steam launch, 6 ft 8 in. beam and also called *Dragon Fly*, was constructed for him in 1895. From 1887 to 1901, de Salis travelled a total of 14,340 miles over waterways of England and Wales, mostly in these two boats. In the course of one day in 1898, he passed through sixty-five locks on the Huddersfield Narrow, Huddersfield Broad and Calder and Hebble Navigations. These journeys resulted in the publication of *Bradshaw's Canals and Navigable Rivers of England and Wales*, in 1904, a reference volume still widely consulted.

Converted Narrow Boat

While Victorian and Edwardian explorers of the water-ways occasionally hired working narrow boats for holiday trips, few were permanently converted for living or cruising until the 'discovery' of the canals after World War II. The space offered by a full-length 70-ft narrow boat enables luxurious accommodation to be planned, and a number of these craft make exceptionally comfortable homes. Powered by original or new diesel engines, most narrow-boat conversions are based on hulls built no later than the 1930s. Several, still in fine condition, were launched in the 1890s! While a motorized boat could be bought for as little as £90 in the late 1950s, the same craft might now be worth £2,000 or more. Fully fitted out, the value might rise to £5,000 plus. Lack of suitable hulls has prompted the building of many specifically for pleasure use, yet there are always buyers ready for narrow boats with a working history. The wooden-hulled conversion illustrated is cruising on London's Regent's Canal.

Traditional Canal Cruiser

Shortage of ex-working narrow boats for conversion to pleasure cruisers has prompted the rapid growth of a flourishing branch of the marine industry: construction of craft on traditional narrow-boat lines. Steel hulls provide the best protection against inevitable contact with lock walls and submerged objects. *Amos* was the first of a highly successful series of 32-ft Hawkesbury Class narrow boats, begun in 1971 by Braunston Boats Ltd, and launched at the firm's Grand Union Canal yard near Rugby. An 8-hp Sabb diesel engine is mounted immediately forward of the tiller steering position. A hatch on the counter lifts to reveal a large access well enabling refuse to be removed from the propeller. In addition to a twin-berth cabin at the stern, there is a WC compartment and open-plan galley/saloon, providing two further berths. The bows feature a large open cockpit. Price, fully equipped, is about £4,000.

Wide-Beam Inland Cruiser

The Elysian centre-cockpit cruiser, built by Appleyard Lincoln of Ely, is a typical river boat of the 1970s. Moulded throughout in glass-reinforced plastic, the hull measures 27 ft × 9 ft 6 in. beam × 1 ft 10 in. draught. There are four to five berths, a choice of inboard diesel engines mounted under the cockpit floor and a folding awning over the steering position. Fully fitted and ready to cruise, its price is in the region of £3,500. A number of Elysians are in river hire fleets, such as that shown crossing Lough Derg on the Shannon, and owned by Emerald Star Cruisers of Carrick-on-Shannon. Use of GRP ensures easy maintenance and a complete absence of leaks from which most wooden craft eventually begin to suffer.

Narrow-Beam Canal Cruiser

The 6 ft 10 in. beam Nauticus 22 GRP cruiser from Malcolm Thomas Plastics Ltd, of Alperton, Middlesex, is equipped with four berths and represents a popular type of canal boat whose use has spread rapidly since the mid-1960s. Available for use with an outboard engine, the inclusive cost is just over £2,600. A 1,100-cc inboard engine with stern-drive unit installed increases the price to £3,382. Shallow-draught cruisers like this can travel on every navigable river and canal in Britain, are small enough to be readily trailed behind a medium-sized family car and, with suitable care, can be used inshore.

Canal Marina

The late 1960s and 1970s have witnessed excavation of purpose-built pleasure-boat marinas on the canal network of England to cater for the explosion in cruising. Earlier developments were generally sited in existing basins. Stringent planning controls have been devised by British Waterways, in co-operation with local authorities, to ensure that such developments are in keeping with the visual style and needs of the canals. The example shown here is Whilton Marina on the Grand Union Canal, below Buckby Locks in Northamptonshire. The private development company involved excavated some 125,000 cubic feet of earth to provide space for several hundred cruisers. As well as conventional servicing facilities, slipway and chandlery shop, there is a customers' boat club, bar and restaurant.

Canal Tripping Boat

There are now about twenty-five passenger craft operating on the nationalized routes under the control of the British Waterways Board; in addition, similar vessels are available for scheduled runs or private hire on various other navigations. Capacity of a typical cruiser of the narrow boat type is between fifty and sixty people. Several cruisers are horse-drawn, and the great majority are powered by diesel engines. Many were originally freight-carrying boats, although in recent years brand-new hulls have been constructed. Typical of the canal trippers is *Water Ouzel*, operated by Willow Wren Cruises of Rugby, and generally plying in the Braunston area. Built as motor boat *Sun* for the Grand Union Canal Carrying Co. in 1935, she is of composite construction (steel sides and elm bottom) and was intended to travel in company with butty boat *Moon*. All passenger-carrying boats taking more than twelve people are required to pass Board of Trade safety tests. The photograph shows *Water Ouzel*, with skipper George Walker at the tiller, passing through one of the Braunston Locks.

Pontcysyllte Aqueduct

Easily the most impressive canal aqueduct in Britain, Pontcysyllte carries the Welsh Section of the Shropshire Union Canal over the fast-flowing River Dee at a maximum height of 121 ft. Chiefly the responsibility of engineer Thomas Telford, it was completed in 1805 and is busy with pleasure cruisers navigating this, the ever popular Llangollen Canal. The aqueduct is carried on nineteen stone arches, solid for their lower 70 ft, hollow above; each has a 45-ft span. The waterway itself is contained in a cast-iron trough, 1,007 ft in length. A towpath occupies part of the width of the trough, leaving just sufficient space for a narrow boat to travel. Not least of the attributes of this remarkable structure is the wonderful view obtained down the river valley, Pontcysyllte invariably exceeds expectations.

Wolverton Aqueduct

Locally known as 'The Iron Trunk', this crossing of the River Great Ouse by the Grand Union Canal at Wolverton, Buckinghamshire, replaced a three-arched structure that collapsed in 1808, not many years after the canal had been opened. Approached by a long, straight embankment at each end, the present aqueduct was ready for traffic early in 1811. It stands 35 ft 7 in. above the normal level of the river and the 15-ft-wide iron trough is just over 101 ft in length. Building cost of Wolverton Aqueduct and the supports of brick on each bank of the river and the central stone pier was about £6,000.

Avon Aqueduct

Scotland's Union Canal, built to link Edinburgh with the Forth and Clyde Canal at Falkirk, possesses three notable aqueducts, crossing the Rivers Almond, Avon and Water of Leith at Slateford. All completed in 1822, the Avon is longest and tallest, running for 810 ft with a maximum height of 86 ft. The twelve arches support a stone channel, and general elements of the design, prepared by Hugh Baird, owe much to Thomas Telford's Chirk Aqueduct on the Llangollen Canal near the border between England and North Wales.

Flash Lock

A forerunner of the modern pound lock, where a chamber is enclosed at each end by gates, was the flash lock—also known as navigation weir, staunch, or water gate. Many lasted on British rivers until well into the present century. One of the last survivors could be seen on the Warwickshire Avon until restoration of the waterway demanded its removal in 1961. This was the Cropthorne Water Gate, near Fladbury, photographed in 1896. A whole reach of the river acted as a lock, with a single gate set in a weir. Operation of the paddles enabled water levels in the reach to be changed: a lengthy and time-consuming process, which might take several hours. A similar structure, which can be regarded more as a two-rise lock staircase, can be seen to this day on the Wey Navigation, where it joins the River Thames at Weybridge, Surrey.

Turf-Sided Lock

Among the earliest pound locks opened in Britain, some featured sloping sides covered with grass, with vertical stonework for a short distance between the two pairs of gates. While this method of construction was more economical, it could only be adopted where water supplies were plentiful. There are no examples on canal navigations: only on river-fed waterways including the Wey Navigation in Surrey and the River Kennet section of the Kennet and Avon Canal. Normally, a series of vertical guides composed of steel or timber uprights prevents boats from being stranded on the grass banks when the water level descends. The picture shows Newark Lock, on the mid-seventeenth-century River Wey Navigation, undergoing extensive repairs during the 1960s.

Narrow Canal Lock

The standard dimensions of a narrow lock, of which there are hundreds of examples in England, are such as to admit a narrow boat of about 70 ft in length by 7-ft beam. Most commonly, they are equipped with a single gate at the upper end and a pair of mitre-gates at the bottom. The rise and fall varies from a few inches at stop locks, built to prevent water loss between the canals of different companies, to a massive 14 ft found at Tardebigge Top Lock on the Worcester and Birmingham Canal. The illustration is one of the five Claydon Locks near Banbury, Southern Oxford Canal. In this case, ground paddles are installed at the top and gate paddles at the bottom. This pattern tends to vary between one canal and another.

Wide Canal Lock (*opposite*)

A pair of loaded narrow boats work through Northchurch Lock on the Grand Union Canal in Hertfordshire. This is a wide-beam 'barge' canal between London and a point just short of Birmingham, enabling a boat 14 ft in width to navigate. Each use of a lock like this required about 50,000 gallons of water. Gates at each end are in pairs, with ground and gate paddles to admit water at the top and gate paddles alone at the bottom. When water in the lock has made a level with the canal outside, the gates are opened by leaning on the balance beam: the boatwoman in the picture is closing a lower gate, a child is checking any forward movement of the butty boat by passing a line round a bollard, and the boatman is about to 'draw' a top ground paddle to set the lock filling.

Guillotine Lock

The great majority of British canal and river locks have mitre-gates, opening sideways, like a door. However, some waterways (notably the Rivers Nene, Great Ouse, Cam and Yorkshire Derwent) display gates that rise vertically. Most modern examples were fitted to assist rapid dispersal of flood water. King's Norton Stop Lock, where the Stratford Canal joins the Worcester and Birmingham Canal, was built to prevent water losses from one concern to the other. Guillotines allowed boats to travel either up to the Stratford from the W. and B., or *vice versa*, depending on which canal was at a higher level at any given time. After nationalization brought common ownership of the two navigations in 1948, the need for the lock ceased, and both gates have been permanently raised since. The picture was taken in 1896, when the device was in daily use.

Lock Machinery

A great variety of design styles will be noted in the types of paddle gear and other apparatus enabling canal and river locks to be operated. Most patterns date from the late eighteenth or early nineteenth century and display pleasing examples of functional elegance, combined with rugged efficiency.

The most simple and earliest type of gate paddle: the wooden shutter covering an underwater aperture in the gates is attached to a bar that can be lifted by hand and secured in several positions by passing a steel peg through one of the holes. The only known example is at the shallow Worsfold Gates Lock on the River Wey at Send.

The great majority of manually operated lock gates are opened and closed by pulling on the extending balance beams. Sometimes the closeness of a bridge does not permit these beams to be fitted to their normal length and a winding device such as this revolving drum is necessary. Sheffield and South Yorkshire Navigation, near Rotherham.

A gate paddle at the lower end of diamond-shaped Shipton Weir Lock, where the Southern Oxford Canal joins the River Cherwell. The boatman's windlass (crank handle) is attached to the spindle on the right.

An unusually large ground-paddle mechanism on the Grand Union Canal in Leicester.

Now derelict, some of the most ornate ground paddles will be seen at locks on Somerset's Bridgwater and Taunton Canal. The suspended iron ball acts as a counterbalance.

Bingley Five Rise Locks

Where a canal must overcome a rapid change in levels in a short distance, a series of closely spaced locks can occur, known as a flight. A development of this principle is the lock staircase, or riser, consisting of several locks leading directly into each other, without any intervening pound. One of the best-known examples is Bingley Five Rise Locks at the eastern end of the Skipton Summit Level of the Leeds and Liverpool Canal in Yorkshire. Five individual chambers are linked, where the top gates of one lock are the bottom gates of the lock above. Total rise and fall is 60 ft. One disadvantage is that once an ascending boat has entered the series, it must clear the top before a descending craft can begin its downhill journey. Other spectacular staircases will be found on the Caledonian Canal, the Leicester Section at Foxton and Watford and at Beziers (Canal du Midi, Southern France).

Anderton Vertical Lift

Still at work, a century after its completion in 1875, this astonishing feat of Victorian engineering transfers boats 50 ft 4 in. between the River Weaver and the Trent and Mersey Canal, above, near Northwich, Cheshire. Twin tanks each take a pair of narrow boats or a wide-beam barge and are moved by electric power, which replaced the original system of steam engines operating hydraulic pumps early in the present century. A substantial charge is levied on pleasure craft wishing to use the lift, but this is more than compensated for by the unique experience of making the journey. The Anderton Lift was designed by Sir Edward Leader Williams, an engineer who was to be later responsible for the Barton Swing Aqueduct, carrying the Bridgewater Canal over the Manchester Ship Canal.

Foxton Inclined Plane

As an alternative to locks in situations where there is a very rapid change in levels to be overcome, various types of lifts or inclined planes were devised. Most in Britain became derelict very many years ago, and no planes can be seen working today. The best known, at Foxton, was completed by the Grand Junction Canal Company in 1900, as a by-pass for the adjacent narrow lock staircases, totalling ten chambers, with a 75-ft rise and fall. Two caissons, or tanks, 80 ft × 15 ft × 5 ft deep, were hauled up and down a concrete slope on rails. A pair of narrow boats remained afloat in each

tank, whose ends were sealed by means of guillotine gates. One caisson almost counterbalanced the other, with additional power supplied by a steam engine operating winding drums. Passage time for a pair of craft was cut to twelve minutes. Because traffic was insufficient to merit maintaining a constant head of steam at the engine house, the device went out of use in 1912 and was dismantled fourteen years later. A very similar updated version can be found in France on the Canal de la Marne au Rhin at Arzviller. This can accommodate a 350-ton barge.

Blisworth Tunnel

British canals are noted for their tunnels, constructed where hills could not be passed by altering the route of the waterway, or if a series of locks was impracticable. Some of the earliest bores were not particularly deep underground and indeed several have been converted into open cuttings subsequently. In all, something like forty-two miles of canal tunnel were constructed in England and Wales, of which nearly twenty-two miles are still open to boats. Second longest now navigable is Blisworth, on the Grand Union Canal in Northamptonshire, which extends for 3,056 yds and allows narrow-beam craft to pass, but lacks a towpath. Ventilation shafts cut at intervals introduce fresh air and are seen as a series of brick chimneys over the top. It was opened in 1805, having delayed completion of the through canal route by several years. As built, Blisworth Tunnel was 16 ft 6 in. wide and 11 ft 3 in. from water level to the centre of the brick-lined arch, and the water was 5 ft 9 in. deep. The picture shows a cruiser about to enter the southern end, near Stoke Bruerne.

Dudley Tunnel

At 3,172 yds, Dudley Tunnel, on the Birmingham Canal Navigations, is the longest in Britain available to craft. Opened in 1792, it is little wider than a narrow boat and throughout its commercial history, craft were propelled by 'legging', i.e. boatmen lay on their backs on the deck and pushed against the walls with their feet. Various connections with limestone loading docks underground produced an original tunnel length of 5,208 yds. Closed between 1962 and 1973, Dudley may now only be navigated by the old legging method, as engine fumes could cause a danger of suffocation. The Dudley Canal Trust organizes public trips in narrow boats from time to time. At one point, near Tipton, the bore opens out into Castle Mill Basin, a rocky cavern, open to the sky. Two further underground caves are notable places *en route.* The picture shows one of the leggers who helped move one of two narrow boats through the tunnel at the time of its reopening ceremony in 1973.

Cowley Cutting

Later canals like Thomas Telford's Birmingham and Liverpool Junction section of the Shropshire Union Main Line feature long, deep cuttings through rock. This route was constructed near the end of the canal era, being opened throughout in 1835. Improved engineering techniques, compared with waterways of sixty or seventy years before, enabled huge quantities of spoil to be excavated in an effort to reduce the navigation to the shortest possible distance between its terminal points. Here, at Cowley, near Norbury Junction in Staffordshire, it had been intended to carve a tunnel of several hundred yards, but unstable rock reduced its length to just 81 yds. When you consider that such excavations were undertaken without the aid of modern earth-moving machinery, the achievement is all the more remarkable.

Iron Towpath Bridge

Development of the canal system coincided with a wide-spread use of cast iron as a constructional material. Many later canal bridges, like this one taking the Oxford Canal towpath across the head of Isis Lock, Oxford, were produced in substantial numbers, especially during the 1820s and 1830s. Bolted together in easily transported sections, the ribbed deck is covered with compacted earth and gravel. Note the simple, yet elegant balustrade.

Brick Roving Bridge

In common with most other features of canal design, waterway bridges reveal an astonishing variety. There are two basic categories of bridge: stationary and moving. The most normal type is a single-arched hump-backed crossing in brick or stone, depending on availability of building materials in the immediate locality. The white-washed brick span illustrated is on the Grand Union Canal at Watford, Hertfordshire. Known as a roving bridge, it carries the towpath from one bank to the other. Note the elegant curves of the parapet, lacking in sharp angles which could prevent the free run of a horse-boat towing line.

Decorative Bridges

In just the same way as motorway construction now brings objections from landowners, the coming of the canals was sometimes hampered; consent for the navigation to pass through the estate of a country house would on occasion only be granted if the canal company agreed to provide structures in keeping with the architectural fashions of the time. This resulted in a number of picturesque and elaborate bridges being built.

Above At Drayton Manor, on the Birmingham and Fazeley Canal, circular brick folly towers containing spiral staircases provide a pedestrian crossing, with wooden deck, while a simple swing bridge catered for wheeled traffic and horses.

Below Creamy local stone was used for this ornate Gothic span, carrying a lane over the Grand Union at Cosgrove, near Wolverton, Bucks. The canal thus took on the appearance of a natural watercourse winding through a late eighteenth-century formal landscape.

Lancaster Canal Swing Bridge

The flat-deck swing bridge occurs quite frequently, larger types being moved electrically. Manual opera tion is demanded of this one over the Lancaster Canal at Hest Bank. The structure swivels on a ball race, positioned centrally on the near bank. Tension rods rising to the upright beams can be adjusted to avoid any sagging of the platform which might cause it to jam. Note the lamp bracket, intended to hold a warning oil lantern.

Welsh Canal Bascule Bridge

Requiring no approach embankments, moving bridges were usually cheaper to build, but over the years were often expensive items to maintain. Constructed in timber with iron fittings, this drawbridge over the Llangollen Canal at Wrenbury is opened by a member of the boat's crew hauling on a chain that dangles from the counter-balanced beams. Another, nearby, is raised by rotating a drum, around which the chain is wound.

Vertical Lift Bridge, Ireland

The canals of Southern Ireland boast a number of different designs of bascule bridge. Of greater interest, however, is this very rare type of vertical lift bridge, situated on the Barrow Navigation at Levitstown. An arrangement of toothed wheels and chains, worked by a fixed handle, raises the deck above the water on a rectangular steel framework. As the bridge lifts, counterbalance weights of cast iron descend to the roadway, forming an effective safety barrier that prevents cars being accidentally driven into the water.

Signs and Markers

Canal companies labelled and dated their structures with an almost obsessive concern to establish ownership or make easier the collection of freight tolls. The most durable materials, cast iron and stone, were used, with the result that many posts and plaques can be discovered today. Each is characteristic of the company which erected them and the variety of designs is very considerable.

A splendidly chunky iron mile plate by the towpath of the River Severn at Bevere Lock, Worcestershire.

Most bridges are identified with an iron (and occasionally a stone) number plaque, extremely helpful in establishing your exact location. The Staffordshire and Worcestershire Canal Company added the bridge names as well, using elegant type, cast in relief. This plaque will be found near Penkridge.

GARRATTS LANE BRIDGE

Names, rather than numbers, appear on bridges over the Birmingham Canal Navigations.

While it is likely that most canal signs were prepared in the company's own yards, this pattern was more widely obtainable, being manufactured by a foundry at Stone, Staffordshire, in 1819. Identical posts can be found on the Shropshire Union Main Line, Caldon Canal, Trent and Mersey Canal and by the Holyhead Road in North Wales. That illustrated is situated on the T and M at Barnton, Cheshire.

Boundary markers were erected to show the extent of land in canal company ownership.

In addition to indicating the miles, iron posts throughout the Brecon and Abergavenny Canal in South Wales show halves and quarters. This one is by the flight of locks at Llangynidr.

Mooring Bollards

All sites where boats habitually tied up were equipped with bollards. Thus, wharves and locksides are littered with these pleasingly shaped posts, carved from wood and stone or cast in iron and concrete. Often, they bear deeply cut grooves, resulting from generations of rope-wear.

A tall cast-iron bollard at the head of a toll island on the Birmingham Canal Navigations Main Line in Smethwick.

Lichen-encrusted stone, for boats to tie up while waiting to enter the Crinan Canal at Ardrishaig, Argyll.

Weather-worn but still useful: a wooden bollard carved from a tree trunk, with its square base set in concrete. Pictured by a Grand Union Canal lock.

This rare composite design in wood protected by iron, is alongside Ireland's Grand Canal at Shannon Harbour.

Rural Canal Pub

Boatman's inns are widely scattered throughout the waterways system, frequently with stables attached for the one-time towing horses. Most are unpretentious, friendly places that have become flourishing concerns in recent years with a growth in summer pleasure-cruising traffic. The pretty Swan Inn at Fradley, junction of the Trent and Mersey and Coventry Canals near Lichfield, Staffordshire, is a textbook example. Its architectural style in warm red brick is Georgian. A cottage on the right was doubtless intended for one of the canal workers, while stabling at the other end is now the headquarters of a thriving hire-craft boatyard.

Urban Canal Pub

The awakening interest in waterways, evidenced by the large number of people cruising on them for pleasure and relaxation, has encouraged breweries to develop waterside facilities at existing canal inns. Several completely new ones have opened in recent years. The Longboat, Birmingham, overlooks the top chamber of the Farmer's Bridge flight of locks near the City Centre, and was completed by Messrs Ansells in 1970. It forms the central feature of a waterside walk with restored eighteenth-century cottages and a British Waterways Board shop and information office. Building materials of the pub harmonize with traditional blue bricks of nearby lock chambers and bridges. Two bars are decorated with painted narrow-boat equipment and murals depicting canal life. A third bar has been created in a narrow-boat moored in a dock alongside. The whole area demonstrates how thoughtful reconstruction and landscaping enhances the locality.

Lock Keeper's Cottage, Stratford Canal

Waterway workers—maintenance men, lock keepers and management staff—were generally provided with housing by the navigation companies. Many of these charming buildings survive in spite of wholesale destruction of the more isolated ones in the years that followed nationalization. A bewildering array of designs can be discovered in every imaginable type of building material. Among the most charming are several barrel-roofed bungalows erected by the Southern Stratford Canal in Warwickshire in the early part of the last century. Well versed in constructing the arches of canal bridges, the contractors responsible for these dwellings obviously adapted techniques used on the waterway itself. The resulting cottages thus resemble elongated bridge holes, their ends and sides filled with brickwork. The photograph was taken at Lowsonford, deep in rural Warwickshire.

Bridge Keeper's Cottage, Sharpness Canal

All bridges spanning the Gloucester and Sharpness Ship Canal, between the Severn Estuary and the inland port of Gloucester, are designed to swing open, thus enabling masted vessels to pass by. The waterway was completed in 1827, and in keeping with the architectural fashion of the times, bridgemen were housed in Regency cottages, each one of which is like a little classical temple. Designs vary from one structure to another, but all feature a neo-Grecian portico on fluted Doric columns.

Ellesmere Port Warehouses

Some of the best industrial architecture in Britain can be found in the waterside buildings designed for the storage and distribution of goods that arrived by boat. Plenty of the smaller structures serve as headquarters for pleasure-craft firms or have been converted into attractive homes and clubhouses. Great complexes like the wonderful Telford buildings at Ellesmere Port, Cheshire, seaport for the Shropshire Union Canal, having outlived their original function, are less easily adapted to modern uses. Dating from 1833, the Great Warehouse was composed of three arms in the shape of a letter E. Boats passed directly underneath, enabling their cargoes to be hauled to the first floor. The surrounding basins with cranes, locks, gas lamps and a steam-driven power plant together created the best example of a canal port in Britain. Most regrettably, the Great Warehouse was completely gutted by fire in 1970 and has since been demolished.

Hartshill Maintenance Yard

All the old navigation companies established engineering centres along the line of their waterways: from such yards, maintenance work on locks, bridges and the channel itself was directed. Here, new gates and equipment could be built, boats constructed and serviced, and materials stored. Many of these yards passed into public ownership on nationalization and the great majority continue to perform their original function. The picture shows Hartshill Yard on the Coventry Canal near Nuneaton. This very pleasing complex of brick buildings dates from the early nineteenth century. The main block is provided with iron window frames and a jolly little clock tower rises above a covered dry dock.

Crofton Pumping Station

The summit levels of artifical canal navigations rely on water supplies from a number of possible sources. Either it is gravity fed from streams or conducted from reservoirs via feeder channels. A third possibility that was adopted was to pump water from a lower level. In the canal-building era, this method was achieved by installing water or steam-driven pumps. Crofton Pumping Station on the Kennet and Avon Canal in Wiltshire was erected at the very beginning of the nineteenth century, with the object of lifting water from a natural stream-fed reservoir 40 ft below. The pair of Boulton and Watt beam engines, dated 1801 and 1810, have been restored to working order by volunteer members of the Kennet and Avon Canal Trust. Both operating simultaneously for twenty-four hours, they have a potential pumping capacity of $6\frac{1}{2}$ million gallons. The Station is open to visitors at weekends and can be seen operating in steam on a number of occasions throughout the year.

Canal Lighthouses (*right*)

Unlikely as it may at first appear, there are several canal lighthouses in Britain. Apart from one that is truly inland, on Lough Corrib in the west of Ireland, they mark the entry to navigable waterways from tidal seaways. Constructed during the last century, they would obviously be of considerable help in directing small ships and sailing barges that lacked sophisticated navigation aids.

When Ellesmere Port's charming red brick lighthouse was erected in 1795, showing the way from the Mersey Estuary to the Wirral Line (now part of the Shropshire Union), the Manchester Ship Canal which now replaces the Mersey at this point was almost a century from completion. Total height from the ground to the inverted harebell-shaped roof is 35 ft, while the base diameter is 8 ft.

Scotland's two remaining coast-to-coast canals—the Caledonian and the Crinan——both have lighthouses at each end. The illustration shows that at the Ardrishaig terminus of the Crinan, overlooking Loch Gilp. Its style is distinctly maritime rather than of the canal tradition.

The Derelict Shrewsbury Canal

At their greatest extent the waterways networks of Britain and Ireland totalled about 5,300 miles. Closures over a period of more than a hundred years have reduced this to nearly 4,000 miles. Some of the derelicts are being brought back to life through restoration schemes and these will undoubtedly grow in number in years to come. Yet others offer a forlorn hope for reopening, being partly bulldozed out of existence or blocked by culverted road-bridge crossings. One in this category is the Shrewsbury Canal section of the Shropshire Union, abandoned in 1944. Heavily overgrown for much of its course, there are plenty of attractions for the industrial archaeologist to discover, like this guillotine-gated lock at Hadley Park on the outskirts of Wellington. An excellent guide to these forgotten navigations is Ronald Russell's *Lost Canals of England and Wales* (David & Charles).

Voluntary Restoration

Recovery of derelict navigations is a nationwide activity, where unpaid waterways enthusiasts employ considerable skills and heavy mechanical plant to bring rivers and canals back to life after decades of decay. Work is in progress most weekends at numerous sites. For important schemes, as many as a thousand amateur navvies have been known to assemble for two days' labour. The picture shows some of the six hundred who attended a 'Dig' on the Droitwich Canal at Ladywood Locks, Worcestershire, towards the end of 1973. Two canals, running for six and three-quarter miles between the Severn and the Worcester and Birmingham Canal, were abandoned in 1939. Now a Trust has been formed to bring them back to life by refitting locks and dredging the heavily silted bed. Further details of restoration participation appear below.

The Rebuilt Upper Avon

The greatest waterways success story of recent years centres on the Warwickshire Avon, sixteen miles from Evesham to Stratford. After a century of dereliction, a charitable trust was formed by enthusiasts to build a completely new series of locks and weirs and to dredge thousands of tons of hard rock and silt from the river bed. All this was achieved at a cost of £300,000, the majority from private sources. Under the dynamic direction of Project Manager David Hutchings, who had earlier carried out restoration of the adjoining Southern Stratford Canal, the scheme was virtually finished at the end of 1973. For the first time in more than a century, large sea-going cruisers are now able to journey to Stratford from the Bristol Channel and the Shakespeare Country is served by a waterways circuit comprising the Avon, Stratford and Worcester and Birmingham Canals and the River Severn. Work throughout was undertaken by volunteers, prisoners and the Services. The pictures show a new lock at Stratford, spanned by a series of steel braces to prevent subsidence, and one of the gate-opening mechanisms, a former River Thames lock paddle wheel cleverly adapted by mounting it sideways.

Canal de l'Ourcq, Paris

Completed in 1822, this sixty-seven mile waterway is part canal and part canalized River Ourcq. It connects the Seine in Paris with the small town of Port-aux-Perches and runs mainly over a course that is parallel with the River Marne. This engraving of 1830 shows that strolling along the towpaths and under the Paris arches was even then a fashionable occupation. Note the open horse-drawn barge and beyond it a rowing boat.

Vertical Lift, Canada (*left*)

A system of lakes, rivers and canals, comprising the two hundred and forty-one mile Trent Canal, connects Lake Ontario with Georgian Bay on Lake Huron. It is understandably very popular with pleasure cruisers. In the thirty-three miles of canal, there are forty-two locks, a marine railway (inclined plane) and two hydraulic lifts, similar to that in Cheshire, at Anderton. The lift illustrated is at Kirkfield and raises or lowers craft some 49 ft.

The Rideau Canal, Canada

Now heavily used by pleasure cruisers. Canada's Rideau Canal was constructed by the Royal Engineers to link the Ottawa River with Lake Ontario at Kingston. Finished in 1832, the one hundred and twenty-four mile line has forty-seven locks, many of them arranged in staircases. The engineer in charge was Colonel John By, who gave his name to Bytown, now known as Ottawa. The engraving, published in the middle of the nineteenth century, shows a five-rise series of locks at Bytown, while paddle steamer *Shannon* pauses to take on goods and passengers.

Morris Canal, Inclined Plane, USA

Some of the most spectacular inclined planes to be built on nineteenth-century canals were on the Morris Canal, New Jersey. The waterway ran for one hundred and two miles from the Hudson River, at Jersey City, to the Delaware River, at Easton. A total rise and fall on each side of the summit level was 1,674 ft; this was overcome by twenty-three locks and twenty-three inclined planes. Traffic consisted mainly of carrying coal and iron ore: in 1866 almost 900,000 tons were handled. Boats were constructed in two sections, each part being lashed to a cradle to ascend or descend the inclines, whose rise varied between 100 ft and 35 ft. The picture was published in 1880, and shows an inclined plane at Newark, with twin sets of rails. Cradles were moved by turbine power, with ropes passed round a cylindrical drum. The boats travelled up or down the inclines at between 4 and 5 mph, resulting in a time saving of sixty per cent from end to end of the canal compared with former navigation through conventional locks.

French Canal Barge

Most of the older navigations in France's, 4,700 miles of inland waterway network were brought up to the Freycinet standard, beginning in 1879. This provided lock dimensions of 126 ft × 17 ft 3 in. that could be passed by the French *péniche* (barge) of about 350 tons. Post-war modernization has brought a degree of obsolescence to canals of these dimensions, and much modernization has been completed or is in progress to achieve accommodation for the European superbarge, carrying 1,350 tons. The older waterways still continue to carry traffic, but in decreasing amounts. Similar to *péniches* found throughout the country, but rather smaller than average at 145 tons, is this Canal du Midi barge, travelling through very typical and lovely plane-tree shaded scenery on the Midi, in Southern France.

Ronquières Inclined Plane, Belgium

This longitudinal plane is the most impressive structure of its kind in the world. It was built during the mid-1960s as part of a scheme to modernize the Charleroi–Brussels Canal. Many locks were replaced and the capacity of the navigation increased from 300 tons to 1,350 tons. The plane overcomes a difference in levels of 225 ft, with a five per cent slope covering 1,566 yds. Twin water-filled tanks accommodate one 1,350-ton barge or four 300-tonners, and each measures 299 ft × 39 ft 6 in., with a water depth of 10 ft. Two hundred and thirty-six wheels carry each caisson on two pairs of double rails. The weight of each tank varies from 4,800 tons to 5,700 tons, including water, depending on the levels in the canals at top and bottom. A hydro-electric plant both provides necessary power to operate the tanks and feed electricity into the national grid. By replacing thirty-eight old locks with the plane and ten new ones, a navigation time saving of twenty hours is achieved. There are viewing facilities for tourists, who now number well over a million ever year.

Europe's Largest Canal Lock

With networks able to accommodate 1,350 ton barges, the inland waterways of Europe have been greatly improved and enlarged since World War II. One of the Continent's leading waterway transport nations is Holland, where a large proportion of goods movement inland is by water. On the Rhine—Amsterdam Canal, shown here and built in 1952, twenty-four hour working speeds barges through massive guillotine-gated locks like the Prinses Irene. Such is the demand that, when this picture was taken in April 1972, construction of another, similar lock was in progress alongside on the right.

Cruising on the Canal du Nivernais

Pleasure boating on European rivers and canals is nowhere nearly as well developed as in Britain. Apart from smaller, sub-standard barge routes, most attention is directed to considerations of freight transport. A healthy hire cruiser industry has, however, grown in France during the 1960s and 1970s, with a notable participation of British companies. Boats are available for water tourism in the South (Canal du Midi and adjoining routes), on the River Marne, in Brittany and in Burgundy. This very characteristic view shows a holiday cruiser navigating the very beautiful Canal du Nivernais in the Yonne Valley near Auxerre. A substantial number of holiday-makers come from Britain.

Calendar of Main Events

Dates given for the opening or closing of a waterway refer to the main part of that navigation. In a number of cases additional sections and branches were subsequently opened. In several instances, routes that were closed have since been restored. Many rivers have always been available to boats, although improvements have been made over the centuries.

1121	Roman Fossdyke Canal, Lincs, improved.
c. 1425	River Lee opens.
1481	Pound locks in use in Italy.
c. 1504	Essex River Stour opens.
1566	Exeter Canal opens with first British pound locks.
c. 1571	River Welland opens.
1594	Kent Stour opens.
1639	Warwickshire River Avon opens.
1653	Wey Navigation, Surrey, opens.
c. 1670	Great Ouse opens. Bure, Yare and Waveney Navigation (Broads) opens.
1684	Hampshire Avon opens.
1704	Main section, Aire and Calder Navigation, opens.
c. 1705	Yorkshire Derwent opens.
1710	River Itchen opens.
c. 1714	River Nene opens.
1717	River Tone Navigation opens.
1723	River Kennet opens.
1727	Bristol Avon opens.
1732	Weaver Navigation opens.
1736	Mersey and Irwell Navigation opens.
1742	River Douglas opens. Newry Canal (Ulster) opens.
1750	Upper Medway opens.
1751	River Don Navigation opens.
c. 1757	River Blyth Navigation opens.
1757	St Helens Canal opens.
1761	First section of Bridgewater Canal opens.
1763	Godalming Navigation opens.
1767	Suir Navigation, Ireland, opens.
1769	Shannon Navigation opens. Linton

Lock section, Yorks Ouse, opens.

1770 Driffield Navigation opens. Calder and Hebble Navigation opens.

1771 Droitwich Canal opens.

1772 Staffs and Worcs Canal opens. Death of James Brindley, River Ure and Ripon Canal opens. First section, Birmingham Canal Navigations, opens (additions to 1850).

1773–1801 Improvements to River Trent.

1774 Bradford Canal opens.

1775 Nore Navigation, Ireland, opens.

1776 Huddersfield Broad Canal opens.

1777 Chesterfield Canal opens. Trent and Mersey Canal opens.

1778 Loughborough Navigation opens.

1779 Stourbridge Canal opens. Caldon Canal opens. Chester Canal opens. Dudley Canal opens (additions to 1858). Stroudwater Canal opens. Erewash Canal opens.

1782 Market Weighton Navigation opens.

1787 Tyrone Navigation, Ulster, opens.

1789 Thames and Severn Canal opens.

1790 Forth and Clyde Canal opens. Coventry Canal opens. Oxford Canal opens. Upper Arun Navigation opens.

Barrow Navigation, Ireland, opens.

1792 Shropshire Canal opens.

1793 Monkland Canal, Scotland, opens. Chelmer and Blackwater Navigation opens.

1794 Cromford Canal opens. Leicester Canal opens. Basingstoke Canal opens. Lagan Canal, Ulster, opens.

1795 Wyrley and Essington Canal opens. Nutbrook Canal opens. River Foss Navigation opens.

1795–1808 Ellesmere and Chester Canal opens, including branch to Llangollen.

1796 Derby Canal opens. Nottingham Canal opens. Strabane Canal, Ulster, opens. Tamar Manure Navigation opens. Shrewsbury Canal opens.

1797 Melton Mowbray Navigation opens. Grantham Canal opens. Leics and Northants Union Canal opens.

1799 Ashton Canal opens.

1800 Peak Forest Canal opens. Severn improvements (and subsequent years). Warwick and Birmingham Canal opens. Warwick and Napton Canal opens. River Boyne, Ireland, opens.

1801 Crinan Canal opens.

1802	Stainforth and Keadby Canal opens.
1803	Duke of Bridgewater dies. Oakham Canal opens.
1804	Barnsley Canal opens. Dearne and Dove Canal opens. Leven Canal opens. Rochdale Canal opens. Ashby Canal opens.
1805	Grand Junction, Thames–Braunston, opens. Grand Canal, Ireland, opens. Somersetshire Canal opens.
1806	Royal Military Canal opens.
1808	Manchester, Bolton and Bury Canal opens.
1809	Croydon Canal opens.
1810	Kennet and Avon Canal opens. Wilts and Berks Canal opens. Grand Surrey Canal opens.
1811	Huddersfield Narrow Canal opens.
1812	Upper Sussex Ouse opens.
1814	Grand Western Canal opens. Old Grand Union (Foxton–Norton Junction) opens.
1815	Worcester and Birmingham Canal opens.
1816	Leeds and Liverpool Canal opens. Wey and Arun Canal opens. Stratford Canal opens.
1817	Royal Canal, Ireland, opens.
1818	Pocklington Canal opens.
1819	Sheffield Canal opens. Lancaster Canal opens.
1820	Regent's Canal opens.
1821	Montgomeryshire Canal opens.
1822	Edinburgh and Glasgow Union Canal opens. Caledonian Canal opens.
1823	Bude Canal opens. Portsmouth and Arundel Canal opens. Carlisle Canal opens.
1824	Thames and Medway Canal opens.
1827	Gloucester and Sharpness Canal opens. Bridgwater and Taunton Canal opens. Torrington Canal opens.
1828	Kensington Canal opens.
1830	Hertford Union Canal opens.
1831	Macclesfield Canal opens.
1834	Thomas Telford dies.
1835	Birmingham and Liverpool Junction Canal (Shropshire Union) opens.
1836	Croydon Canal converted to railway.
1841	Ulster Canal opens.
1842	Chard Canal opens.
1844	Birmingham and Warwick Junction Canal opens.

1845	Thames and Medway Canal converted to railway.
1850	Newry Ship Canal opens.
1853	Droitwich Junction Canal opens. Carlisle Canal closes.
1857	Shropshire Canal closes.
1859	River Bann and Lough Neagh Navigation opens. Corrib Navigation, Ireland, opens. Ballinamore and Ballyconnell Canal opens. River Foss closes.
1867	Chard Canal closes.
1868	Wey and Arun Canal closes.
1869	Ballinamore and Ballyconnell Canal closes.
1875	Anderton Lift completed. River Adur closes.
1877	Melton Mowbray Navigation closes.
1878	River Parrett Navigation and Westport Canal close.
1885	Mersey and Irwell Navigation closes.
1890	Erne Navigation opens.
1891	Bude Canal closes.
1894	Manchester Ship Canal opens.
1896	Upper Arun closes. Portsmouth and Arundel Canal closes.
1900	Foxton Inclined Plane opens.
1904	Somersetshire Coal Canal closes.
1905	New Junction Canal (Aire and Calder) opens.
1906	Start of Royal Commission on Waterways.
1914	Wilts and Berks Canal closes.
1927	Thames and Severn Canal closes.
1929	Formation of Grand Union Canal Co.
1931	Ulster Canal closes.
1935	Yorks Derwent closes.
1936	Grantham Canal closes.
1937	Nottingham Canal closes.
1939	Droitwich Canals close.
1944	Huddersfield Narrow Canal closes. Cromford Canal closes. Montgomeryshire Canal closes. Shrewsbury Canal closes.
1946	Inland Waterways Association formed.
1948	Many waterways nationalized in England, Scotland and Wales.
1950	First National Rally of Boats, Market Harborough. Monkland Canal closes.
1951	Lagan Canal closes.
1952	Rochdale Canal closes.
1953	Barnsley Canal closes.
1954	Stroudwater Canal closes. Upper

Bann Navigation closes. Tyrone Navigation closes.

1950 Newry Canal closes.

1961 Dearne and Dove Canal closes. Royal Canal closes. Manchester, Bolton and Bury Canal closes.

1962 Forth and Clyde Canal closes. Chesterfield Canal closes (but part still open).

1963 St Helens Canal closes. British Waterways Board formed.

1964 Derby Canal closes. Southern Stratford Canal reopens.

1966 Runcorn and Weston Canal closes.

1967 River Tone Navigation closes.

1968 Northern Lancaster Canal closes. Transport Act: Cruising, Commercial and Remainder categories established for nationalized waterways and Public Right of Navigation removed

1972 Grand Surrey Canal closes

1973 Newry Ship Canal closes to commercial traffic. Droitwich Canals restoration begins. Dudley Tunnel reopens. Montgomeryshire Canal restoration begins.

1974 Regional Water Authorities established in place of various river authorities (England and Wales). Government-appointed Water Space Amenity Commission set up. Ashton and Lower Peak Forest Canals reopen. Upper Avon Navigation reopens. Basingstoke Canal restoration begins.

Waterways Museums

The Waterways Museum, Stoke Bruerne, near Towcester, Northants. Telephone Northampton 862229. Open every day except Christmas and Boxing Days and Mondays during the winter. This is Britain's national waterways museum, established and run by the British Waterways Board since 1963. Situated in a most attractive village on the Grand Union, with flight of locks, Blisworth Tunnel, thatched inn and well-stocked canal souvenir and book shop, it is well worth making a day excursion to Stoke Bruerne. The collection is particularly strong on narrow boats and their traditional painted decorations. But there are also many other items, boat models, photographs and various fascinating relics showing the history of more than two centuries of inland waterway transport.

Llangollen Canal Exhibition, Llangollen Wharf, Denbighshire, N. Wales. (Information from Market Drayton, Shropshire, 2641.) This display aims to tell the story of the canals from their building to present times by means of a series of panorama. Especially interesting for parties of school children and students, it is run in conjunction with horse-drawn boat cruises to the Pontcysyllte Aqueduct.

Exeter Maritime Museum, The Quay, Exeter, Devon. Telephone Exeter 58075. Open all year except Christmas and Boxing Day. Since 1969, this collection in old warehouses alongside the Exeter Canal has featured many types of small craft from various parts of the world. There are several traditional pleasure craft, the Bridgwater Dock drag dredger (above), inland fishing coracles from the Severn and Welsh rivers and a Bude Canal tub boat equipped with wheels for use on that waterway's inclined planes.

Crofton Pumping Station, Crofton, near Great Bedwyn, Wilts. Information from Mr N. Reynolds, telephone 01-948 1577. Open Sundays and, in steam, certain weekends throughout the year. See above.

National Maritime Museum, Greenwich, London SE10. Telephone 01-858 4422. Closed Christmas Eve, Christmas and Boxing Day and Good Friday. Inland exhibits include Thames steam launch *Donola* (above), a Manchester Ship Canal steam tug and a reconstructed traditional Thames pleasure-boat building yard.

Goole Museum, Carlisle Street, Goole, Yorks. Telephone Goole 3784. Open throughout the week. There is material relevant to the inland port of Goole, with photographs, models and paintings.

Manchester Museum, Oxford Road, Manchester 13. Telephone 061-273 3333. Closed Good Friday and Christmas. Several canal boats and models can be seen, with some examples of traditional narrow-boat painted ware.

South Yorkshire Industrial Museum, Cusworth Hall, Doncaster, Yorks. Telephone Doncaster 61842. The collection of domestic and industrial

relics of the region includes a waterways room.

The Science Museum, Exhibition Road, South Kensington, London SW7. Telephone 01-589 6371. Closed Good Friday, Christmas and Boxing Day. In addition to photographs of inland craft, there are a number of boat models.

The Black Country Museum, information from Dudley Museum and Art Gallery, St James's Road, Dudley, Worcs. Telephone Dudley 56321. Now being formed at an open-air site near the Tipton end of Dudley Canal Tunnel, exhibits are to include various canal structures, buildings and bridges, together with boats and other relics.

Ironbridge Gorge Museum, Southside, Church Hill, Ironbridge, Telford, Shropshire. Telephone 095-245 3522. Open Monday to Friday, or by appointment. A huge open-air museum of industrial archaeology which is being extended all the time: it covers about a square mile. An iron tub boat and restored inclined plane lift on the Coalport Canal can be seen with other evidence of eighteenth-century iron smelting.

Morwellham Quay, Morwellham, near Tavistock, Devon. Telephone Gunnislake 766. Open throughout the year. An area of intense waterway activity with inclined planes on the Tavistock Canal, the portal of a canal tunnel and old photographs of local commercial boating all preserved.

Hull Maritime Museum, Pickering Park, Hessle Road, Hull, Yorks. Telephone Hull 27625. Closed Good Friday and Christmas and Boxing Day. Among the maritime exhibits is a section devoted to Humber sailing keels.

Maritime Museum for East Anglia, Marine Parade, Great Yarmouth, Norfolk. Telephone 0493 2267. Open June to September. Broadland boats, including sailing wherries, can be seen in model form.

City of Liverpool Museums, William Brown Street, Liverpool L3 8EN. Telephone 051-207 0001. Closed Christmas Day and Good Friday. There is a good collection of ship models, including Mersey and Weaver flats and other local waterway craft.

Manchester Ship Canal Co. Museum, Ship Canal House, King Street, Manchester 2. Telephone 061-832 2244. Open on application only. The collection deals with all aspects of Britain's most modern waterway.

North West Museum of Inland Navigation, information from E. Paget-Tomlinson Esq., Clifton House, Top Road, Kingsley via Warrington, Lancs. In the process of formation, probably at Ellesmere Port, where the Shropshire Union Canal meets the Manchester Ship Canal. The Museum aims to preserve various inland waterway craft, including narrow boats, an ice breaker, a Norfolk wherry and a Mersey flat.

Useful Addresses

Many waterways in England, Scotland and Wales are under Government control, being managed by the *British Waterways Board*. BWB has offices throughout Britain, and full information will gladly be supplied on application to their headquarters at Melbury House, Melbury Terrace, London NW1 6JX. Telephone 01-262 6711.

For information on routes not under the control of BWB, seek advice from *The Inland Waterways Association*, 114 Regent's Park Road, London NW1 8UQ. Telephone 01-586 2510/2556. Re-organization of waterway management and the formation of a series of Regional Water Authorities for England and Wales, dealing with many navigations previously in the care of various river authorities, was carried out in 1974.

Details of navigation bodies in the Republic of Ireland may be obtained from *The Inland Waterways Association of Ireland*, Dr A. Delany, Fourways, 58 Seafield Road, Clontarf, Dublin 3. For Ulster, consult B. Magee Esq., *River Bann Association*, 66 Lodge Road, Coleraine, Northern Ireland. (Or, in each case, the appropriate Tourist Board in Dublin and Belfast.)

Spread of individual waterway associations and societies means that the time is fast approaching when each river and canal in Britain will have its own volunteer body. As details of officers tend to change, you are advised to contact the leading organization, IWA, at the above address. The IWA was founded in 1946 and now has a membership well in excess of ten thousand individuals. Apart from promoting better standards of waterways maintenance for all classes of amenity use, the Association has saved many canals and rivers from dereliction or closure. Its Inland Shipping Group is a highly respected and knowledgeable body of experts who provide information on commercial waterway transport and are pressing for its greater use in Britain. Everyone with any kind of interest in rivers and canals should become a member of the IWA, thus supporting the Association's work while enjoying various benefits otherwise not available.

Brief List for Further Reading

Information on waterways abroad, especially cruising facilities, can be obtained from the appropriate Government Travel Offices in London.

Among voluntary waterways bodies, one that especially deserves mention is the *Waterways Recovery Group*. This organization co-ordinates all enthusiasts' restoration work, and publishes details of working parties staged in all parts of Britain, in its bi-monthly journal, *Navvies*. For further information, write to Graham Palmer Esq., WRG, 4 Wentworth Court, Wentworth Avenue, Finchley, London N3 1YD.

There are very many guides, histories, maps and other publications produced on inland waterways. The Inland Waterways Association at 114 Regent's Park Road, London NW1 8UQ, will provide a list, on request, of most titles currently available. These may be bought personally or by post from the Association. All proceeds are devoted to the IWA's publicity and restoration campaign.

General

L. A. Edwards, *Inland Waterways of Great Britain* (Imray and Wilson)

John Gagg, *The Canallers' Bedside Book* (David & Charles)

John Hankinson, *Canal Cruising* (Ward Lock)

Robert Harris, *Canals and Their Architecture* (Hugh Evelyn)

A. P. Herbert, *The Water Gipsies* (Methuen)

Eric de Maré, *The Canals of England* (Architectural Press)

Hugh McKnight, *The Shell Book of Inland Waterways* (Shell/David & Charles)

Hugh McKnight and David Edwards-May, *The Canal Enthusiasts' Handbook* (David & Charles)

L. T. C. Rolt, *The Inland Waterways of England* (Allen & Unwin)

Ronald Russell, *Lost Canals of England and Wales* (David & Charles)

Cruising Guides

The Inland Waterways Guide (IWA/Boat World Publications, annually)

E. and P. W. Ball, *Holiday Cruising on the Thames* (David & Charles)

L. A. Edwards, *Holiday Cruising on the Broads and Fens* (David & Charles)

Charles Hadfield and Michael Streat, *Holiday Cruising on Inland Waterways* (David & Charles)

Hugh McKnight, *Ladyline Cruising Guides*—1, Llangollen; 2, Oxford; 3, Shropshire Union; 4, Grand Union (North); 5, Grand Union (South); 6, Grand Union (Leicester); 7, Staffs & Worcs; 8, Trent & Mersey and Caldon. Other titles in preparation.

Gerard Morgan-Grenville, *Holiday Cruising in France* (David & Charles). Other Continental titles in preparation

Nicholson's Guides to the Waterways—1, South East; 2, North West; 3, South West; 4, North East; 5, Midlands; 6, Scotland (Robert Nicholson/BWB)

P. Ransom, *Holiday Cruising in Ireland* (David & Charles)

Journeys Described

Frederic Doerflinger, *Slow Boat Through England* (Allan Wingate)

Frederic Doerflinger, *Slow Boat Through Pennine Waters* (Allan Wingate)

John Gagg, *5,000 Miles, 3,000 Locks* (Arthur Barker)

John Liley, *Journeys of the Swan* (Allen & Unwin)

L. T. C. Rolt, *Green and Silver* (Irish waterways) (Allen & Unwin)

L. T. C. Rolt, *Narrow Boat* (Eyre & Spottiswoode)

John Seymour, *Sailing Through England* (Eyre & Spottiswoode)

John Seymour, *Voyage Into England* (David & Charles)

E. Temple Thurston, *The Flower of Gloster* (1911) (David & Charles reprint)

Inland Boats

Tom Chaplin, *A Short History of the Narrow Boat* (Hugh McKnight Publications)

Roy Clark, *Black Sailed Traders* (Norfolk wherries) (David & Charles)

Alan Faulkner, *The George and the Mary* (Grand Union Co. narrow boats) (Robert Wilson)

G. Frere-Cook, ed., *The Decorative Arts of the Mariner* (colour section on narrow boats by Hugh McKnight) (Cassell)

Edgar J. March, *Spritsail Barges of Thames and Medway* (David & Charles)

Hugh McKnight, *Canal and River Craft in Pictures* (David & Charles)

Edward Paget-Tomlinson, *Mersey and Weaver Flats* (Robert Wilson)

J. Wilson, *Fenland Barge Traffic* (Robert Wilson)

Robert Wilson, *The Number Ones* (Midland narrow boats) (Robert Wilson)

Historical

J. H. Boyes, *The Canals of Eastern England* (David & Charles)

Anthony Burton, *The Canal Builders* (Eyre Methuen)

V. T. H. and D. R. Delany, *The Canals of the South of Ireland* (David & Charles)

Charles Hadfield, *British Canals* (David & Charles)

Charles Hadfield, *The Canal Age* (David & Charles)

Charles Hadfield, *The Canals of the East Midlands (including part of London)* (David & Charles)

Charles Hadfield and Gordon Biddle, *The Canals of North West England* (David & Charles)

Charles Hadfield, *The Canals of South and South East England* (David & Charles)

Charles Hadfield, *The Canals of South Wales and the Border* (David & Charles)

Charles Hadfield, *The Canals of South West England* (David & Charles)

Charles Hadfield, *The Canals of the West Midlands* (David & Charles)

Charles Hadfield, *The Canals of Yorkshire and North East England* (David & Charles)

Charles Hadfield and Gordon Biddle, *The Canals of North West England* (David & Charles)

Jean Lindsay, *The Canals of Scotland* (David & Charles)

W. A. McCutcheon, *The Canals of the North of Ireland* (David & Charles)

Henry de Salis, *Bradshaw's Canals and Navigable Rivers of England and Wales (1904)* (David & Charles reprint)

Index